Tales of a Hull City Police Recruit

Ron Sagar

Highgate of Beverley

Highgate Publications (Beverley) Limited
2000

British Library Cataloguing in Publication Data.
A catalogue record for this book is available from the British Library.

© 2000 Ronald Sagar

Ronald Sagar asserts the moral right to be identified as the author of this work.

ISBN 1 902645-19-7

Published by

Highgate of Beverley

Highgate Publications (Beverley) Limited
4 Newbegin, Beverley, HU17 8EG. Telephone (01482) 886017

Printed by

Abbotsgate incorporating **ba**/print/

4 Newbegin, Beverley, HU17 8EG. Telephone (01482) 886017
Unit 3, Northumberland Avenue, Kingston upon Hull, HU2 0LN. Telephone (01482) 225257

Author's Preface

Beneath the tedious, poorly paid, routine and sometimes inept management in the Hull City Police in the 1950s there was a quite proud and honest-to-goodness police force doing its best to attend to the needs of the Hull public. At the same time individual officers had to handle the incredible disciplinary demands placed upon them by the Chief Constable, Mr. Sidney Lawrence, with great care and tolerance. The Chief was a man who was feared by practically everyone in the force. Nevertheless, history shows that before his arrival in June 1948 the force was far from efficient, but when he left in June 1962 Hull City Police had become one of the most efficient and proud forces in the country.

I joined Hull police on the last day of December 1956. I knew no one in Hull and simply chose to join the city force because it was roughly half-way between my home in the south of England and my wife's home in Scotland. I knew nothing of note about police work but I did hold a great schoolboy ambition to become a detective. Of course, before realising that ambition I had to complete a mandatory two years as a constable on beat duty. This book is about becoming a constable in Hull in those far-off days and some of the foolish and quite absurd incidents I encountered during two years as a beat constable. All the events are based on true happenings but I have changed many names and some places in order to avoid causing any embarrassment.

Police work has changed drastically since I was introduced to policing in the 1950s and the incidents that occurred in those days are almost all unrepeatable, already vanished, and with absolute certainty will never return.

Finally I have to say that I remain proud to have been a member of the Hull City force for the 18 years before the force was amalgamated to become Humberside Police in 1974. Whilst this book tells tales of some ineptitude in the force in my early days, there are many stories on record elsewhere about policemen of Hull which relate to really first-class police work with dedicated policemen of all ranks upholding the law in the true traditions of the British bobby.

Ron Sagar

Young PC Graas

Contents

Joining the Hull City Police

It was the autumn of 1956 and Airman Roland Graas was stationed at RAF Castlerock, in County Londonderry, Northern Ireland. He was newly married to a gorgeous dark-haired Aberdonian girl and just three months away from demobilisation after five years, RAF service. Hankering after a different way of life, he decided that perhaps the police service would provide an interesting career. Wearing a uniform troubled him, though, for after RAF service he just did not like the restriction of personal activity that uniform demanded. It is fair to say that he knew very little about police work but thought that maybe he could go straight into the CID. After all, he wasn't very tall and felt that to be in uniform he would be dwarfed in a crowd of people taller than he was – even with a helmet on his head.

He met his wife in her home-town in the far north of Scotland and, as he came from the south of England, the question of where the couple would settle down could be something of a problem. They were living in a delightful bungalow beside the coast of Northern Ireland and he did not wish to remain in the RAF: a new career decision was needed and needed quickly.

One evening the couple studied a map of the British Isles and, looking down the east coast of England, they realised that Kingston upon Hull was about half-way between their two families. With no more ado they decided that Hull would be a suitable place to settle down. Did Hull have a police force of its own, though? Roland knew Hull was a city because he had seen the name Hull City in the Third Division North of the Football League. He also knew Hull and its docks had been heavily bombed in the Second World War, and that he had once watched some smelly fish wagons pass through Crewe railway station, but he knew precious little else about the place. Thinking about his future he felt that the only way to find out if the city had its own police force was to write and see if they would like him to join them. That night, in his very best handwriting, Roland wrote to 'The Chief Constable, Hull, Yorkshire.' He explained that he was soon due for demob from the Intelligence Section of the RAF and wanted to join the police in Hull, not only because he had heard that the force had a good reputation but also that the Chief Constable was a very good man too! Actually he knew nothing of the force and did not even know the Chief Constable's name. He made a conscious decision not to mention that he was hardly tall enough to be a policeman, at least he was not as tall as any policeman he had ever seen anywhere, even in London, where he had heard that Metropolitan Policemen were often described as Metronomes. He posted the letter later the next day at a letter-box near the Portstewart police station. He was nervous, for he had never written to the police before, let alone to a chief constable, and maybe he was chancing his luck by writing that he had heard that the Chief was a good man! Soon afterwards he wished he hadn't included the patronising bit, for it was not in Graas's nature to patronise anyone.

One evening about two weeks later a rather large and chubby constable from the Royal Ulster Constabulary called at Graas's bungalow. 'We have some papers from the Home Office wid your name on. They is askin' us to arrange fur yues to come to station ta sit exam to join the police somewheres in England. Can yues come to station tomorrow evening? an sit the exam?' asked the officer.

Graas agreed and arrived at the police station about seven o'clock the following evening. The desk sergeant greeted him warmly and continued, 'Over there is Constable O'Malony. He is tryin to do yer exam papers. He's a bright one is that one. Educated at Ballykelly High School he was. We is tinkin that if ye both get same answers yues is going to pass fur sure. It says 20 minutes fur a wee bit o writing – dictation they English is callin' it. But see we's no dictation nothing. Yues just copy it wid all the commas and full stops in the right places and put a few o them capital letters where yues can. Fur sure yues got nothing to worry about – and don't worry about that 20 minutes' limit printed on the paper. To be sure there's no bloody Home Office man in here lookin' at the clock this night. In any case clock's been broken for weeks.'

Graas soon completed the dictation test in neat joined-up writing by simply copying from the paper the sergeant kindly placed in front of him. No one dictated a word.

Then came the arithmetic test. 'Yues just start the sums yourself,' grunted Constable O'Malony, scratching his head as he pondered over the first question.

'Can yues see that one about 9 and a cross and 9?' he muttered. 'Yes,' replied Graas. 'I am past that one. It's 81. Nine nines are 81.'

'To be sure it could be that,' came the reply. 'But them Home Office people is clever alright. See that cross could be to multiply, but there again it could be the cross to add up and make it just 18. My advice to yues is to write down the 8 clearly like, and then, to be sure, put a line right down the middle of the 8, so it'll have them Home Office bastards thinkin a wee bit if yues meanin' 18 or 81. And don't let them catch yues out with callin this lot mathematics – they's only sums dressed up a wee bit.'

When the 'examination' was over Graas asked the desk sergeant why he was apparently so concerned about the Home Office. 'Them people rules the police and sets the recruits questions all over England. They poke their noses into all police work over there. It says Home Office Entrance Examination at top of the paper as well. The Home Office knows nothing about police work, you mark my words.'

Graas asked the sergeant if he knew anything about Hull. 'No, but I heard it was badly bombed in the war and it's got some docks, so I guess it must be at the seaside somewhere. I was in England on a course not many weeks ago. One of the men training with me was from Hull, mind. He used to say that Hull – I think he called it Kingston upon Hull – has got a chief constable who thinks he's God almighty himself. Then he told me that the men in the force think he's related to the devil himself. Whatever he is, that man told us that his chief is a man called Lawrence and that he's got a frightening reputation for discipline. Even his superintendents are scared stiff of him. I would think if yues go there you'd best be careful.' About ten days later Graas received a letter from Kingston upon Hull City Police recruiting sergeant – a man called Grand. Sergeant Grand. The letter stated that he had passed the entrance examination with 90% for the arithmetic and an amazing 100% for the dictation. 'Good heavens,' thought Graas, 'they will think I am much more clever than I really am.' He had never obtained 100% in anything before, not even in the tenderfoot tests in the Boy Scouts.

In his letter the sergeant pointed out that it had not been necessary to subject Graas to the usual recruits intelligence test because they had checked RAF records and found that he was working in the Intelligence Section of the RAF!

Graas also saw by the letter that the address was given as Kingston upon Hull City Police, Alfred Gelder Street, Hull, so he now had no fears of being moved about some county area against his will if he joined the city force. The final paragraph invited him to attend Hull Central Police Station at a time to suit him. The purpose was to go for a medical examination by the Hull City Police surgeon, Dr. Percy Scott. Apparently Hull police did not trust the RUC to arrange the medical. However, Graas decided that he was now on his way to being a police constable and would do his best to become a member of Hull City Police. That night he watched Dixon of Dock Green on a neighbour's black and white television, thinking that he could begin to learn as much as possible about the police and be prepared to answer any crafty questions the recruiting sergeant might ask when he had the medical examination. He few days later he left his wife in Ireland and by bus, boat and train travelled to Hull. It was about 4.30 am on a dark, cold and foggy Tuesday morning in October 1956 when Graas arrived by train at Hull Paragon Station. He had Sergeant Grand's letter safely tucked away in his blazer pocket. For several minutes the station was busy as about a dozen or more people got off the train. They all seemed to know where they were going as they hurriedly walked through the station concourse and away into the early morning gloom. Graas quietly followed some of the people to a side entrance. He glanced about, saw the Regal cinema across the road and waited there for a couple of minutes. There was bound to be a policeman in the street any minute, he thought. When he saw one he would tell him that he had come to join his police force and then, no doubt, the policeman would welcome him and walk with him to the Central Police Station, wherever that was. The lads in the station would no doubt shake his hand, let him try a helmet on, hold pair of handcuffs or a truncheon and make him a cup of tea. They would know about his 100% dictation test, he thought, and no doubt admire him for his effort. But now he was getting cold and there was not a single policeman to be seen anywhere. He wandered back into the station. After a minute or so he walked to the opposite side of the station and waited on the steps of the Tower Cinema for about fifteen minutes, saw no sign of any policeman and then walked back into the station concourse where it was still and lifeless but a bit warmer. Feeling slightly dejected he tried the rear door of the Royal Station Hotel but it was locked. Then saw a policeman standing smoking at the top of the steps leading to the gents' toilet opposite Smith's bookstall. Strolling up to the officer Graas said, 'Hello. I have come to join the Kingston upon Hull City Police Force.'

'So what?' he said gruffly. 'What are you telling me for? Do I look like I'm a bloomin recruiting sergeant? Look at me helmet, lad. It says British Transport Police on me badge, doesn't it? I'm not one of them clever city dicks.'

'Can you tell me where the Central Police Station is, then? Graas asked.

'Look, you bloody greenhorn, that lot treat us Transport police as we're nothing but bloody night watchmen. Last time I arrested a bloke for pinching some fish from fish dock I had to wait for them to come and check my evidence. Damned clever lot. They told me I didn't have any evidence and made me let the bloke go, gave him the fish back as well. Halibut it was. Nicked halibut at that. I look the other way now and don't nick anybody any more. They won't make a fool of me again, I'll tell you!'

'I'm sorry about that,' Graas said. 'But can you tell me where the Central Police Station is?'

'Listen, I can't believe you are wandering about here at this hour of the night wanting to join any police force, let alone Hull. I'm helping nobody to join this lot. Good night.'

With no more ado the policeman took one or two more puffs at his cigarette, threw the cigarette end to the ground and walked off in the direction of the Tower cinema. That was the last Graas saw of the very first Hull person he met.

Not knowing the city, or where he could find the police station, Graas eventually found a taxi driver dozing in a taxi at the front of the Paragon Station entrance and asked to be taken to the Central Police Station. Unknown to Graas, the street-wise taxi driver quickly realised that Graas had no idea of the whereabouts of the police station and proceeded along Jameson Street and on along George Street, over North Bridge, through Witham, and then along Holderness Road. Sitting in the back behind the driver, Graas was dismayed to see the low-lit and shabby streets of east Hull with the smoke-filled fog billowing about as the taxi drove on through the empty streets. It seemed a long way to the Central Police Station but Graas was comforted by the way the driver seemed to know where he was going.

Looking out into the fog, he saw a police box in the middle of the dual carriageway on Holderness Road. Just then the taxi turned into a road Graas saw by a sign as being Maybury Road. Must be getting near Alfred Gelder Street soon, he thought. On they travelled, through Marfleet, Hedon Road, Drypool Bridge and then into Alfred Gelder Street, where the taxi finally pulled up outside the police station. There was practically no traffic about and, apart from two or three office cleaners and a postman making their way to work, he saw nothing of the citizens of Hull.

'That will be 19s. 6d,' said the taxi driver. Graas gave him a £1 note and feeling glad to be there, told him to keep the 6d. change. Graas had been well and truly taken for a ride.

The old Alfred Gelder Street police station was quiet and the foyer deserted when Graas walked in through the swing doors. Looking about, he saw a bell beside a window marked 'Enquiries'. He rang the bell but the window remained shut. Getting no answer, he took a seat on a wooden bench nearby and waited. Looking around, he saw that there were some lights on in a back office behind the enquiry window and he could hear the slow tap-tapping of a typewriter. Apart from that, it all appeared very still inside. After a few minutes he began to look for a toilet. There must be one near, he thought; policemen must surely call in the station to go to the toilet. The first door he opened alongside the foyer was into a broom cupboard and, as he opened it, a broom fell out and clattered on to the stone floor of the foyer. He picked it up and then tried a door that he found opened into an unoccupied office. A further rattle of the bell failed to rouse anyone so he began to climb up the stone stairs leading from the foyer, thinking that there would be a toilet up there. He had only gone a few steps up when a voice behind him shouted, 'Hey, sergeant, we've got a burglar in our midst.'

Graas spun around. Burglar! He had not seen a burglar, but if there were one about, it would be the very first burglar he had seen, and what an impression he would make if he were the one to make the arrest!

Just as the thought crossed his mind, a burly sergeant appeared at the bottom of the stairs. 'Doesn't look like your usual burglar to me,' he said.

'You are a cheeky blighter nipping in here in the middle of the night. What are you up to?' questioned the constable looking up the stairs at the startled Graas.

'Goodness me. I haven't nipped in anywhere,' spluttered Graas. 'I have come to join the police. I am not a burglar.'

'You can join us alright, in the cells, that's where you can join us. We can't have burglars joining the police force, lad. You've been caught red-handed trying to break into one of the offices. I heard one of the office doors creaking a minute ago. It must have been you. There's no one else here,' said the constable.

Graas saw that the constable had his hand poised ready to pull at the strap of his truncheon in the truncheon pocket of his trousers so he nervously stepped down the stairs saying, 'I'm not a burglar. I have just come from Ireland to join your police force and I was looking for a toilet. I did ring your bell.'

'We don't ring bells to get into toilets, not in Hull we don't. If you rang the bell we would have heard it, that's what we're here for,' scoffed the sergeant.

'Do you see, sergeant, he's got a tie on – and a nice white shirt. Never seen a night-time burglar in a tie before,' commented the constable. 'Looks more like a young con man than a burglar.'

Graas began to protest his innocence, but the policemen did not appear to listen. 'Under the Judges' Rules I have a duty to caution you,' said the constable. 'You are not obliged to say anything unless you wish to do so, and whatever you say will be taken down in writing and may be given in evidence. Now then, I have heard some stories in my time. By the sound of your accent you are not even Irish, let alone coming in here to join the police force in the middle of the night. Let's not tell stories, shall we. So what the hell are you doing sneaking in here? There's not much to pinch in a police station, you know.'

'You had better get all this in your book, constable. You'll be charging this clever little devil with something before the night's out,' said the sergeant.

Graas then did his best to explain that he was in the RAF stationed at Castlerock in Northern Ireland. He had in fact travelled by train from Castlerock to Belfast, then by boat across the Irish Sea before catching a train across England to Hull, where he had arrived just a short while ago. It was the only time he could catch a train that connected with the boat from Belfast. In any case, the boat had been delayed for hours because of fog in the Irish Sea. He then showed the two officers his boat and train tickets. They both examined them and, as they did, Graas remembered his letter from the recruiting sergeant. Delving into his blazer pocket he produced the letter, and, smiling broadly, he handed it to the sergeant.

'Where does it say that you should come here in the middle of the night, lad? Anyhow, you are never big enough for this job. Brawn is what we need in this force. You don't seem to have much of that, do you? Better stay in the RAF if you ask me. You look a right little Brylcream boy,' said the sergeant.

'So I don't have to lock him up then, sergeant?' asked the constable.

'No,' he replied with a smile. 'Not unless we lock him in the cells until the recruiting sergeant deals with him.'

'I shall not put anything in my book then, sergeant. Fancy trying to join police at this hour. Maybe he thinks we are well paid or something,' added the constable.

'But we do meet 'em in this place. I bet his mother doesn't know he's out like this at night, and practically nicked for burglary too.'

'As it happens, this is the time my delayed boat and train connections got me here,' said Graas. No one appeared to listen but the constable directed him to a toilet and later gave him a mug of tea, telling him to sit in the foyer until the recruiting sergeant reported for duty about 9 am in about three hours' time.

Shortly afterwards Graas heard the sergeant and the constable go off duty. He was disappointed that they did not even say cheerio to him. Other officers replaced them. Graas saw one of them peer into the foyer from the enquiry office window, laugh, and, upon closing the window, say to someone inside, 'He must be crackers coming in here in the middle of the night. He must have been drinking.'

Shortly afterwards a woman began cleaning the foyer floor with a mop and a bucket of water. 'The sergeant and his mate are laughing about you in there, son,' she said, 'making fun of you, they are, saying nobody will be able to see you under an 'elmet and that you came here in the night and asked to join up. I don't believe a word of it. You can't be that daft!'

It was a long and chilly three hours waiting there before the kindly-looking recruiting sergeant – a Sergeant Grand – approached him. 'I am told that you have been waiting here since before six o'clock this morning,' he said. 'I understand you are the airman from Castlerock in Ireland.'

'Yes, I am,' was the eager reply.

'You were damn good with the dictation test,' said the sergeant. 'I have never seen a 100% result in that paper before.'

Graas blushed slightly as he acknowledged the praise but said nothing. He did feel guilty, though, well just a little bit guilty. 'Now listen,' continued Sergeant Grand. 'You are here for a medical. I did not expect you so soon after I had written, but never mind. I can check your height and weight and I can also check that you can expand your chest up to a minimum of two inches. That's the rule. I can check for any colour blindness too. You see you would be no good to us if you couldn't tell the difference between red, amber and green at traffic lights. And it would be no good if you were to describe a stolen bike as green if it was black, now would it?'

'No, it wouldn't,' agreed Graas.

'The police surgeon must carry out the medical examination, check your privates and all that, and your lungs, of course. If we are satisfied with you you will have to go along to Morrill Street clinic for x-rays. If you pass you can join us. This is a proud force, you know. We don't let any old riffraff in. Any questions?'

'No. I am just tired after travelling for so long, that's all,' he replied.

'Do you mean you came over here during the night? Why didn't you go to your relatives of friends and get some sleep and come back this afternoon.'

'I've never been to Hull before, sergeant, and I don't know anyone here,' he replied.

'Never known of anyone joining us who had never been here before. Hull can be a rough place for policemen. It's really tough at times, you know,' advised the sergeant.

He then began to look Graas up and down as they made their way to the sergeant's office on the first floor. 'Are you sure you are at least five-feet nine-inches tall, lad? Looking at you I am not too sure.'

'Yes. I am,' replied Graas anxiously.

'We will soon check it out,' commented the sergeant.

They had now entered the sergeant's office above the foyer. A wooden measuring stand about seven-feet high stood against a wall. 'Take your shoes off then. Shoes could give an extra couple of inches and we can't have that, can we, lad. It would be cheating,' said Sergeant Grand.

Nervously removing his shoes, Graas walked over to the measuring stand. The sergeant watched as Graas carefully stretched up and positioned himself as tall as he could. He felt the slide measuring bar come to rest on his head as the sergeant announced that he was just five feet nine and one half-inch tall. Fortunately Sergeant Grand could not manage to look at the top of the measure and at Graas's stocking feet at the same time so Graas just managed to raise his heels unnoticed, making up about three quarters of an inch to be sure of being above the 5 feet 9 inches height requirement. The remaining medical tests went well, particularly the expanded chest test. He managed this easily, having spent a fair amount of time in the RAF doing gymnastics and taking many heavy-breathing exercises and early morning runs along the Londonderry and Antrim coast.

Dr. Percy Scott, the elderly police surgeon, appeared later in the morning. He appeared more concerned about why Graas wanted to join the Hull force than he was about the medical. Nevertheless, the medical test went well. Telling the good Scottish doctor that Hull was about half-way between his home in the south of England and his wife's home in Aberdeenshire home seemed to fascinate the doctor. He said that he had never heard of such a situation before. 'Fancy, your wife is a Scot. That's marvellous. We could do with a few more of the right kind of Scots in Hull,' he explained. 'The Hull St. Andrew's Society could do with some young blood.'

Given directions to the Morrill Street Clinic, Graas took his first daylight walk through the Hull streets. It looked better in daylight, especially as the night fog was now lifting. Not having had any breakfast he bought a bottle of milk from a milk float delivery-man and drank it as he sauntered along Holderness Road, feeling pleased that he had got over his main worry – the height test. Being five feet nine and a half made him feel good too. He was barely five feet eight in the RAF.

The x-rays revealed no problems and shortly afterwards he returned to the Central Police Station where he saw Sergeant Grand once more. The sergeant told him that he had telephoned the clinic and found that all was well with the x-rays and that he was now clear to join the force. No one had asked him how long he had to go to his RAF demob date, but when he told Sergeant Grand that his demobilisation was three months away the sergeant appeared very annoyed. 'What in the name of common sense did you come here in the middle of the night for when you have three months in which to do it. Write to me when you are demobbed, then I will arrange a suitable date for you to start your training. Don't ever come here in the middle of the night again. Next time wait until I tell you the time and the date you should come.'

'Yes, thank you, sergeant. So can I be introduced to the Chief Constable today then?' Graas asked politely.

'The Chief, the Chief, what next? Good God, lad! You really don't know much about this job, do you? Many a sergeant would run all the way to Beverley and back again to avoid seeing the Chief and here's you, a real whippersnapper of a would-be recruit, asking to be introduced. You have a lot to learn you have. Start now by learning that you don't refer to him as the Chief. He's the Chief Constable. Get it? He would eat a recruit like you for breakfast. And no, you can't be introduced. No chance!'

Roland Graas left the police station shortly after mid day, disappointed that he had not seen the Chief Constable but happy in the knowledge that when he returned he would become a policeman. He was concerned that he had apparently upset Sergeant Grand, though, and decided that he would send him a postcard from Ireland to let him know he had arrived safely.

An oldish-looking constable with many wartime medal ribbons on his chest gave him directions to Paragon Station. As he walked through Queen Victoria Square he realised that the early morning taxi driver had well and truly conned him. However, he reasoned that when he became a policeman he would look out for the taxi man and advise him to mend his ways. Maybe he would make him his first arrest too.

As the train steamed through west Hull Graas naturally reflected on his first day in Hull. Was he doing the right thing joining the Hull force and bringing his wife to live in the city? His thoughts were compounded by the fact that the first policeman he met in the city was not a real policeman at all but a British Transport bobby who did not like the Hull City force. Was there more to his disliking city policemen than the stolen halibut story? The first taxi driver he met was obviously dishonest and the first city policemen he met accused him of being a burglar. On top of that he was not given the chance to meet the Chief Constable. As the train rumbled away from Hull and along the Humber foreshore he wondered just what sort of place and what kind of people he was letting himself in for.

Time alone would tell.

Sworn In

It was 30 December 1956 when Graas returned to Hull and found lodgings at 32 Savery Street. He reported to the City Police HQ in Alfred Gelder Street, as instructed, at 11.30 am and before lunchtime he had been measured for a uniform. His head was measured as $6^7/_8$ths but somehow the helmet appeared to cover not only his head but a fair proportion of his chubby little face too. A size $6^3/_4$ was tried but it just sat on his head like a skullcap.

'No,' said the uniform issue clothing officer. '$6^7/_8$ths is your size. You will get used to it. The helmet gives a man confidence, you know, but I just hope that you don't become cross-eyed with the front tip of it being right there before your very eyes. We can't have cross-eyed policemen in the force, at least not in Hull City.'

On completion of the issue of his uniform with its buttoned-up-to-the-neck jacket, thick double-breasted overcoat and heavy black cape, Graas was told to return to police HQ at 9 am the following morning, for, at 10 o'clock he would be sworn in as police constable 129 before the Stipendiary of Kingston upon Hull, Mr. D. N. O'Sullivan. It would be 31 December 1956.

At the duly appointed time Graas stood proudly to attention in the witness box at the Magistrates Court in the Guildhall and, reading from a prepared statement, declared to the magistrate, 'I Roland Graas declare that I will well and truly serve our Sovereign Lady Queen Elizabeth the Second in the office of constable for the City and County of Kingston upon Hull, without fear or affection, malice or ill will, and that I will, to the best of my power, cause the peace to be preserved, and prevent all offences against the persons and properties of Her Majesty's subjects, and that while I continue to hold the said office I will, to the best of my skill and knowledge, discharge all the duties thereof, faithfully according to law.'

Mr. O'Sullivan congratulated him on his appointment and wished him well in what he described as a splendid force. Graas did not know it then but he and O'Sullivan were to see a great deal of each other in the years to come. However, that afternoon Graas asked the recruiting sergeant once more if there was a chance that he could be introduced to the Chief Constable. 'Forget it, 129. If he sees you I'll get a rollicking for letting such a little chap into the job. Do me a favour, lad; never let that mop of hair at the top of your head be cut short. As it is, it just gives you the edge on making you just, but only just, the minimum height for this job.'

A few days later he was on his way to the Police Training Centre at Newby Wiske, near Northallerton, North Yorkshire. Three other trainee constables from Hull joined him on the 12-week course. Instruction was given by experienced uniformed sergeants and inspectors, which gave the young hopefuls an insight into police practice and procedure, numerous legal terms and definitions, powers of arrest, criminal law, evidence and road traffic law. Just as the English language is huge and complex, Graas found that it comes but second to the complexity of the English legal system; in fact, he felt more than once that learning legal definitions parrot-fashion was particularly nauseating but, of course, having an exact knowledge of the legal meaning of words such as larceny, burglary and the like did have its benefits. One morning in the classroom the instructor asked Graas to stand up and give the definition of a pedestrian-controlled vehicle. Sensing the need to introduce a little humour into the classroom, Graas stood to attention and in an Irish accent replied, 'A pedestrian-controlled vehicle is a vehicle controlled by a pedestrian.' The whole class began laughing and the sergeant immediately threw a piece of chalk at Graas but missed, and then shouted out, 'That's not the legal definition, Graas, and you know it. If I had my way I would ban RAF humour in the police. Ex-RAF men like you always seem to look at life as if it's all fun and laughter. I'm telling you now you won't be smiling when you walk beats in Hull. Sidney Lawrence will see to that. Now sit down and don't ever use that silly Irish accent in here again.'

Later Graas's instructor – a tall, hard, and cruel-faced sergeant from the Newcastle-upon-Tyne City Police Force – was quick to question Graas's height before telling him that he would have no chance of a police career in Hull once the dockers knocked the stuffing out of him. At the risk of annoying the sergeant once more, Graas told him that the day was fast arriving when brains more than brawn would be the order of the day in the police force.

Despite the sergeant's attitude towards him, Graas enjoyed the course for the most part but he felt that the daily sessions of drill were boring and, in his opinion, a waste of time. Spending hours practising the positions of the body when standing to attention, at ease and when standing easy seemed particularly inept when practically everyone on the course had served their time in National Service in either the navy, the army or the Royal Air Force. There were no females on the course, in fact, from what Graas had heard, there were few women in the whole of the police service. However, the instructor appeared duty-bound to give his description of the kind of drill he required of the recruits. 'When you are on duty and standing to attention the feet will be turned out at an angle of about 30 degrees, the heels together and in line with the knees braced. The trunk will be erect and the weight borne evenly on both feet. Shoulders will be level and square to the front, down and moderately back. The breathing must not be restricted in any way. The head will be erect, chin in, eyes looking straight ahead, neither up nor down. Arms will be at the side and hanging naturally with the elbows and wrists straight. Hands will be curled up but not stretched. The thumbs will be facing the front with all the nails clean and manicured. The position is one of readiness. This position will always be used when addressing a senior officer.'

He continued, 'When standing at ease the feet and heels will be about 12 inches apart with the arms straight and elbows braced. The hands will be behind the back with the right hand held slightly between the fingers and thumb of the left hand and resting in its palm. When standing easy the body will be free to move at will, but a police officer must never slouch. Slouching can sometimes cause the helmet to fall off the head.'

One frosty cold morning, as the recruits were standing easy just before drill practice began, Graas questioned the instructor on the position regarding looking straight ahead, and not up, nor down, when addressing a senior officer. 'I have seen a senior officer here at the training school who stands at least 6 feet 7 inches tall. If, as you say, I am expected to look straight ahead when addressing him I shall be looking straight at his rib cage. If such an officer was a woman then I could be accused of ogling her breasts or even worse.' Upon hearing Graas's comments the other recruits could not contain themselves and many burst into uncontrollable laughter. 'Shut up, shut up! Control yourselves! Stand to attention with your mouths shut!' shouted the red-faced instructor. 'What do you think you are training for Graas? The lunatic brigade?' Marching up to Graas and looking down at him he continued, 'You, Graas, in order to look senior officers in the face, you will have to learn to stand on your toes, won't you? Instructions must be obeyed in the police force, and in Hull, with Sidney Lawrence in charge, the sooner you learn that the better. One more thing, if you ever again attempt to turn this squad of recruits into a mob of laughing policemen you will end up in Scarborough in one of those seafront arcades stuffed as a blooming laughing policeman and nothing more.'

Drill, and more drill then followed, and it went on for over an hour with the instructor adding an extra fifteen minutes to the session during the normal morning tea-break period. 'No cups of tea for you this morning, you lot. We can't have laughing policemen on the parade ground can we? Makes me angry, it does. Young policemen must learn to take things seriously all the time and you will now, now you have not had a cup of tea.'

At that time – in the 1950s – the police were experiencing difficulties attracting suitable recruits. The training sergeant's general attitude to them did nothing to lessen their disenchantment with pay and conditions, and it was not uncommon for young policemen to leave of their own accord before the completion of their probationary period. Graas was enjoying the challenge and had no intention of joining them, no matter what the old-fashioned attitudes and difficulties were.

In due course the training came to an end, Graas came sixth out of the 32 recruits. He was happy with the result; in fact, his happiness was overflowing at the thought of seeing the back of the drill instructor. He was now looking forward to his wife joining him and settling down to his new career in Kingston upon Hull.

It was now the spring of 1957. Harold Macmillan was telling everyone they had never had it so good. Most of Hull city centre had been rebuilt after the war damage. The Hull City Police was preparing for a visit by H.M. the Queen and His Royal Highness The Prince Philip, Duke of Edinburgh, on 18 May, but that was much too important a matter for a young and inexperienced P.c. Graas to be involved in.

In those days Kingston upon Hull City Police consisted of about 500 constables, 90 sergeants, 20 inspectors, half a dozen superintendents an assistant chief constable and, of course, one Sidney Lawrence. The City covered about 17,500 acres and contained a little under 295,000 inhabitants. P.c. Graas learned that he was posted to eastern division where there was a strength of 90 constables, a dozen sergeants, four inspectors, a chief inspector and a superintendent. There were no CID men actually under the control of the division as they were all under the control of the Head of CID and operated from the CID HQ in Queens Gardens.

The City Police HQ was now moving out of the old HQ in Alfred Gelder Street and other offices in the Town Hall chambers and the Guildhall. Central Division moved from Parliament Street and the City CID moved from Grimston Street too. Now for the first time they were all being housed in the grand purpose-built offices in Queens Gardens. Everyone should have been happy at the thought of working in the new offices, charge room, cell accommodation and so on, but Sidney Lawrence's name figured prominently in canteen chatter at the time. The thought of the Chief Constable actually being in the same building as the CID and Central Division filled everyone there with foreboding and Graas soon realised that the comments made about Sidney Lawrence in Ireland and at the training school were not said in jest.

In his naivety Graas had always thought that a chief constable would be something of a paragon of virtue, admired by his men and the public in general but he couldn't understand how his chief constable was feared by just about all the men, particularly the superintendents. 'You see,' said one experienced constable, 'the superintendents can't avoid him. They have to report to him almost every day and I reckon he often telephones them with questions just to keep them on their toes. You will learn how he affects every one. He even has his driver take him about the City to spy on constables to see if they are gossiping, leaning against lampposts or looking slovenly. You can be in trouble even if you take your helmet off to give your head a bit of a scratch. When he sees something – anything like that – he goes back to his office and telephones the divisional superintendent, tells him that his men are not up to standard – because he has seen something that he considers below standard – and then gives the superintendent a rollicking, usually telling him that he is not up to his job. Knocks the superintendent sideways, it does.'

Graas was glad to know that he was to work on beats in east Hull, where the divisional HQ was at Crowle Street. Out there he would probably never come into contact with the apparently much feared Mr. Lawrence. However, he was still rather disappointed at never being given the chance to at least be introduced when he was accepted into the force. Maybe he would have the chance to give the Chief a friendly wave if he ever saw him driving by. 'Don't ever do that,' one constable advised. 'It would be more dangerous than waving a red rag to a bull, and a mad bull at that.'

On completion of the initial training the practice for all new constables' introduction to practical police work in Hull was to spend the first three weeks walking beats on night duty with an experienced constable. The tours of duty started at 9.45 pm and ended at 6 am The 15 minutes before was actually unpaid time but was demanded by the Chief Constable in order that constables could get acquainted with the happenings on their patch and check on current crime activity before setting foot on the street at 10 o'clock prompt. The three weeks, described by some cynics as working in the dark, was thought by those in authority to give a new officer an opportunity to learn the geography of the various beats in the division. Also, it was said, it would give him the chance to get used to wearing his uniform in public and balancing his helmet properly on the top of his head. Trouble was, after midnight most members of the public were at home and in bed.

One of the first experienced constables to take Graas out on a beat was a constable with more that ten years service in the city. He had also seen war service in the Royal Navy. He was also a well-educated, articulate, judicious and capable man, but fairly new to eastern division. He told Graas that until recently he had worked on beats in western division but had fallen foul of Sidney Lawrence. He went on to say that Sidney lived in a detached house in west Hull and that it was the responsibility of the constable on that particular beat to carefully and quietly examine Sidney's house twice every night between 10 pm and 6 am. The idea was to help prevent any chance of a burglary there. He explained that he had been on night duty one night during the winter when there was a two-to-three-inch snowfall. That night he had arrested two petty criminals for stealing a bicycle and had also attended two road accidents. A domestic disturbance also demanded his attention and the beat included a number of shops and other vulnerable property that he considered important to examine. All this work and the necessary hand-written reports took time. The tour of duty passed quickly and it was time to report off duty before he had had time to examine the Chief's house.

When the Chief Constable drew his bedroom curtains and glanced out of the window shortly after seven o'clock that morning he was surprised to see that there had been a snowfall sometime during the night. Looking up the garden path he also saw that there was a set of footsteps up to and away from his front door and realised that they were made by the newspaper delivery boy. A few moments later, as he let his scraggy ginger cat out of the back door, he became increasingly disturbed as he noticed that there were no footsteps in the snow around other parts of the garden paths or indeed near the garage. The night-duty constable had obviously neglected his duty by failing to examine the house for signs of burglars during the hours of darkness. Realising such neglect, Sidney was furious. Whoever the night-duty constable was, he was in for big trouble. How could any junior officer fail to attend such an important duty? Didn't he care about the most important man in the Hull police force? After all, what could possibly be more important than protecting the Chief's home and family against the criminal fraternity of Hull?

Sidney immediately telephoned the divisional superintendent, who was at that time having a shave in readiness for the day ahead. Sidney demanded an explanation for the neglect of duty but none could be given. The superintendent had only just let his own cat out, let alone found out what had, or had not, been happening in the division during the night. How could he? Nevertheless he was told to have an explanation double-quick and in any case before Sidney arrived at his office at 8.30 am.

The night-duty constable was now at home nicely tucked up in bed, quite oblivious to the Chief's observations and anger. Very few constables had the luxury of a telephone at their homes in the 1950s but the lack of communication did not deter the divisional superintendent in the least. He knew that he would be the subject of more of the Chief's tongue if he did not have an answer to the lack of footsteps in the snow problem by 8.30 am. So with no more ado, he telephoned his division at Gordon Street and ordered a constable to take the divisional bicycle and go to the off-duty and sleeping constable's home on the outskirts of west Hull to tell the unfortunate man to return to divisional HQ immediately to explain verbally, and in writing, why he had failed to examine Sidney's house during the night.

On passing the superintendent's instructions to the now awaked constable, the Pc with the message suggested that maybe the way out of the problem was to say that the snow did not fall until after 6 am that morning, but neither of them knew at what time the Chief had discovered the lack of footprints around the house, so they quickly abandoned the idea. They also knew that the Chief occasionally drove his car about the City during the night to count how many constables he could see walking about the various streets.

The snow had turned to slush by 8.20 am when the tired but anxious and very annoyed constable set off for Gordon Street on his bicycle. Meantime, as he peddled on, Sidney telephoned the superintendent twice at his home and then at Gordon Street before losing all patience when the superintendent was as yet unable to explain the constable's failure. Bellowing down the 'phone, the Chief said that any failing by the constable was ultimately the superintendent's failure too! Did the Superintendent not appreciate the embarrassment the Chief Constable would be subjected to if, above all others, his house was burgled? Just imagine the fun the *Hull Daily Mail* would make of it. Didn't he have the ability to control the men under his command? Would he not be better doing the constable's job himself? Apart from the night-duty officer's lack of attention, Sidney now viewed the failure to check his house as a neglect of duty on the part of the night duty supervisory sergeant and inspector as well, as they had neglected to supervise the examination of the house. The Superintendent was also to blame, said Sidney, as he failed to ensure his supervisory officers carried out their duty efficiently.

Sidney continued to blast away at the Superintendent until the Superintendent managed to get a word in to tell him that the night duty constable had apparently been fully occupied during the night but had now just been seen propping his bike against a wall outside. He was now at Gordon Street. 'I shall give you three minutes to get his explanation, then ring me back,' said Sidney. Then he added loudly, 'You can tell him he is posted to eastern division and he will start there at 9.45 tonight.' 'But that will mean that he will have to travel from his home in west Hull all the way across the city, sir,' protested the Superintendent.

'He's got a bicycle, hasn't he?' replied Sidney as he banged the telephone down. The thoroughly disenchanted, tired and miserable constable told his rather sympathetic Superintendent that he had, in fact, been fully occupied throughout the night with various tasks that were more demanding of his time than checking the Chief's house. In any case, the house had never been burgled and was unlikely to be, as everyone knew the Chief lived where he did and, if the policeman of Hull were in fear of him, what chance had a burglar got? Furthermore, the supervisory night duty inspector and sergeant would vouch for the busy night he had had. The was no doubt that the Superintendent sympathised with him, but the constable realised the Superintendent was powerless to do anything about the posting to east Hull.

The constable submitted his written report, detailing his work during the night, and the Superintendent gave the details first in brief and then in full to the chief. Sadly, it was all to no avail. The Chief Constable had seen with his own eyes that the constable had failed to examine the house and that was all there was to it. He believed that in the interest of good discipline in the force a punishment was necessary. The Chief decided that it would not be fair to put the constable on a discipline charge because the Chief could hardly be witness, complainant and judge, and, therefore, the constable would be posted to the opposite end of the city from where he lived. The cycling there and back would be the punishment.

In the Chief's view the posting would also help the citizens of Hull because they would now have the benefit of an additional aid to policing by having the presence of an extra policeman cycling across the City each day.

'There will be plenty the police training centre will not have told you about being a policeman in Hull, you know,' said another old policeman one day. 'For instance, if you are feeling unwell, Sidney Lawrence can deduct money from your pay if you follow to the letter the policy he has laid down for anyone reporting sick. You see, if you are reporting sick, say you have been assaulted, or maybe fallen off your bike and you go off duty sick because you just can't carry on. Well, the instruction is that you must get a medical certificate from your own doctor that first day. The certificate must be sent to the Chief's office that first day without delay. Failure to obtain a medical certificate on the first day of absence will result in a deduction being made from your pay. The deduction will be made without warning and with no redress. God only knows how you are expected to get to your doctor, obtain a certificate and have it delivered to the Chief's office the same day when you are sick. Maybe he thinks we have all got bloody homing pigeons.'

Summonses, Is That all?

By the end of April 1957, P.c. Graas was allocated his first beat and instructed to work the 6 am to 2 pm shift. Sergeant Lindsey Doyle was his first supervisory beat sergeant. Doyle was described by other constables as one of the old school – whatever that could mean – but he was a crafty old devil too who appeared to be pre-occupied with trying to catch the constables malingering or taking short cuts between streets on their beats so as to save walking too much.

The beat working system in east Hull in the 1950s was arranged so that beat officers worked on what were known as fixed beats. These were arranged in such a way that as much of the actual beat area as possible would be patrolled on foot in any given hour. The purpose of the system was also designed to enable the supervisory sergeants and inspectors to have a rough idea where to find the beat constables as they patrolled along specifically planned routes. In Sidney Lawrence's view the system also ensured that any lazy constables did in fact walk their beats instead of possibly wasting their time out of public view drinking tea in some back street café or terrace house kitchen. Any constable found by his supervisors neglecting his beat in some such way was likely to be the subject of a discipline charge before the Chief and fined, or worse.

In fairness, however, the vast majority of constables considered the fixed beat system a good system and worked their beats with enthusiasm and efficiency, proved by the fact that they kept the crime rate at a very low level. Most constables knew their beats and the people living on the patch a good better that his counterpart in beat patrol cars nowadays. In the late 1950s Hull policemen worked beats that were either specified 'foot' or, in a few cases, 'bicycle' beats and the public often gave bits of information about wrongdoers

19

to the officers they knew well. Many people were proud to do so. The bicycle beats generally covered the outskirts of the City and the new corporation housing estates of Longhill and Greatfield and were operated by older constables, whose legs were perhaps not quite up to the pace demanded by the foot beat system.

People seemed to care more for each other and their property then, particularly those living in the thousands of modest little terrace houses. This was especially so in places like Courtney Street, Nornabell Street, Barnsley Street, Buckingham Street and similar streets on the opposite side of Holderness Road.

Beat constables were given a choice of several clearly defined hourly routes to patrol during the eight-hour shifts. They were required to telephone the divisional HQ when reporting for duty at a section box to let the station sergeant know they had arrived on duty and to state which route was to be taken hour by hour. The chosen route would include about half a dozen fixed points – usually at road junctions – that the constable would have to pass en route during the hour. He would select a different route for the next route and so on, and telephone his divisional HQ at a pre-determined time each hour. Quite often at these call times the station sergeant would pass messages to the constables that were relevant to his beat work. Such messages would be about suspect or stolen vehicles, local crime being reported and messages of various kinds including messages of someone's sudden death in the Hull area or other parts of the country to be passed on to relatives. Household telephones were few and far between in those days.

Pc Graas's first beat patrol on his own commenced at the Holderness Road section box situated between the overhead railway bridge at Burleigh Street and Nornabell Street. Walking in an easterly direction his first 'point' was the Holderness Road/Village Road junction. He then took what he considered a pleasant walk through Garden Village. As he proceeded past the Garden Village Boys' Club building in the middle of the 'village' he caught a glimpse of Sergeant Lindsey Doyle peeping out at him from behind some curtains in the Boys' Club. Good grief, Graas thought, why is the sergeant spying on me? Anyone would think that I am a burglar, not a policeman. However, Graas pretended he had not seen him and walked on, trying his best to look smart and efficient. The next point was at the Endymion Street/Dansom Lane junction, and then on he went along Dansom Lane to Courtney Street and then up Courtney Street to Holderness Road and back along Holderness Road to the section box. Apart from a few early morning workers cycling to work, all was quiet. In fact, he had observed nothing untoward and no one had even asked him the time. As he approached the section box Sergeant Doyle came up behind him. 'You are just over two minutes late getting back here, 129. It is just after seven o'clock. The route you have taken can easily be patrolled on foot in an hour. You have not been gossiping have you? he enquired officiously.

'No,' replied Graas. 'I haven't seen anyone to gossip with.'

'Unless you have been summonsing somebody, or attending a road accident or some such incident you have no excuse for being late. And just you remember that gossiping with the constable on the next beat is a disciplinary offence. I hope I don't catch you gossiping, 129. Remember you are on probation for two whole years and it is part of my duty to make sure that you make an efficient constable. If not, you will not complete your probationary two years. Do you understand?'

'How could I fail, sergeant? Yes. Of course, I do, but I haven't seen the constable on the next beat, let alone speak to him.' Then Graas asked curiously, 'I must say though, sergeant, gossiping is one thing, but surely, as I am very new to this job, if I see a constable on another beat I can talk to him maybe to ask him anything I might need to know?'

'You ask *me*. I am the one to ask,' replied Sergeant Doyle sharply.

'I find this gossiping question difficult to understand, sergeant,' said Graas. 'You see, I don't see how you can prove two constables are gossiping just if you see them talking to each other. After all, it could be that they are talking about some important policing matter.'

'Now leave that to me as to what is proved and what isn't. I know when a constable is malingering and when he is not. I know east Hull and you will find that there are times when I shall be keeping an eye on you when you will not know I am there. It comes with experience, you see, and that is something you have not got. Now then, have you issued a summons against anybody yet? No, you won't have. There are thousands of cyclists in this city and many of them have the audacity to ride bicycles with inefficient brakes and faulty lights. You had better get on and find some faulty brakes cyclists and report them. I shall leave you now as I have important work to do.' And so the sergeant pedalled away along Holderness Road on his old and rusty 'sit-up and beg' Raleigh bicycle.

Alone under his helmet once more, Pc Graas telephoned Crowle Street HQ to give the next beat route he was about to take. The morning rush hour traffic was now beginning to build up on Holderness Road. Graas was not feeling too sure of himself but he hoped that, should a nasty accident occur, he would be able to deal with it and deal with it quickly before Sergeant Doyle appeared. He stood at the corner of Barnsley Street and Holderness Road with his back to the Elephant and Castle pub doorway, where a cleaner was scrubbing the step. 'Good morning, lady,' he said cheerfully.

She pulled a half-smoked cigarette from her lips and said, 'What do you bloody want? Damned coppers, all cheerful and nice in the morning, aren't yah? Why aren't you so bloody friendly all the time instead of hanging around here at night waiting to catch us serving drinks after hours, then? We don't want you lot saying good bloody morning to us, thank you very much.' Taken aback by the cleaner's attitude Graas was speechless and simply wandered off along Barnsley Street, then across to Buckingham Street, eventually making his way along Laburnum Avenue and back onto Holderness Road. William Jackson & Son Limited at the corner of Severn Street was now opening up for the day and so was William Cussons, the little grocery and provisions shop on the corner of Barnsley Street near to the Elephant and Castle. Gradually gaining in confidence at every stride, he was now ready to put into practice all he had learned in his recruit training.

There were now frequent trolley buses going along Holderness Road and hundreds of cyclists pedalling to work. Some had small petrol-driven motors fitted precariously above the rear and sometimes the front mudguard to give the wheel an extra touch of speed to the ordinary pedal power. Was it fair to stop any of them to check their brakes? Graas thought it rather petty to do so when they were hurrying to work and considered it more important to make himself known to the various shopkeepers instead, for he felt that he needed to introduce himself to some of the people on his beat and get to know them.

Who knows, he thought, he might want to use their telephones sometime to telephone divisional HQ in an emergency.

The shopkeepers made him feel welcome, although one woman did embarrass him when she said with a smile, 'You are too little and baby-faced to be a real bobby.' Walking past several people standing at a bus stop a few minutes later Graas said, 'Good morning. Are you all well?'

'What's it bloody look like? We're waiting for a bus, not a bloody ambulance,' retorted a grumpy middle-aged man in a flat cap and scruffy raincoat. No one else spoke but Graas did catch the eye of a grossly overweight woman of about 40 years who scowled at him as he did his best to smile and appear friendly. Another woman, wearing a dirty white turban around a mop of greasy ginger hair, shrugged her shoulders and looked blankly down at the kerb as he walked on. Just then he heard one of the women say, 'Cheeky devil, who does he think he is? He's not from Hull, got too posh a voice. Young coppers, they'll do you one minute and make out they are friendly the next.'

His chatter with shopkeepers took longer than he anticipated, so in order to catch up on time on the designated route and be on time for his next hourly call to Crowle Street, he took several short cuts through back passages, trusting to luck that Sergeant Doyle would not be on the lookout. He needn't have worried. Sergeant Doyle had a puncture in the front tyre of his bicycle whilst in Church Street, Sutton, and would be some time before he got back to Holderness Road.

Shortly before nine o'clock a young schoolgirl came running up to Graas carrying a little Yorkshire terrier that she said she had found. Recalling his training he obtained the girl's name and address, saw that there was no name or address on the dog's collar and took the dog from the little girl. 'I have got some string, mister,' volunteered another little girl. 'You can have it for a dog lead if you want.'

'Yes, that's a good idea, thank you,' replied Graas as he was handed the length of string. As the children ran off to school Graas carefully fastened the string around the little dog's neck and began to walk the dog to the Holderness section box. There he could telephone Crowle Street, tell the station sergeant that he had a found dog and ask for someone to collect the dog and take it to Crowle Street to await collection by the people from the Clough Road Dogs' Home.

As he walked – and sometimes tugged – the terrier along the pavement two young women came walking towards him. They were laughing and pointing at the dog.

'We've never seen anything so funny in all our lives as such a little bobby doing his patrol with such a little dog. Poor little dog, he looks too scared to be a police dog. I hope you haven't been hurting him. Why haven't you got a proper dog lead for him? Poor little thing.'

Feeling very embarrassed Graas replied, 'He's not a police dog. He is a found dog. I am just taking him in.'

'Taking him in! You haven't nicked him, have you? Let him go, that's what you should do. He will find his own way home, he will. Anyway, how do you know he's a found dog? He has to be lost before he can be found. Did he tell you he was lost then?' The two women began laughing again, and, partly leaning against each other in their laughter they began to walk away. 'You can tell he's a new one, can't you? His helmet don't look as if it's been in the rain,' he heard one of them say as they continued their laughter down the street.

Telephoning Crowle Street, Graas said, 'Hello, sergeant, it's Pc Graas. I've got a found dog. I am at Holderness Road section box. Can you arrange for a van to come and collect it? It's a Yorkshire terrier.'

'Well, well, well,' replied the station sergeant. 'Here we are with 129 Graas on his first beat and he's very well. He's actually found a dog. A Yorky dog too. Not a big ferocious dog, mind, just a little Yorky – and wants transport to go and collect it to give it a nice little ride – all at taxpayers' expense.' Oozing with obvious sarcasm he continued, 'He wants transport for a dog and I haven't even got transport for Sergeant Doyle and his old bike. Do you realise that your sergeant has had his bicycle front tyre blow out and now he's got to push his bike and walk all the way to Witham to get a new tyre? No, you wouldn't know, would you? How do you know the animal is lost, 129? In my long and varied service in the police force I have never ever known a dog to speak, let alone come up to a policeman and tell us he's lost. Maybe you can teach me something. If it speaks put it on the phone right way. I will ask it some pertinent questions.'

'No, of course, it doesn't speak, sergeant, but a little girl told me it was lost and I have brought it along for safe keeping.'

'They are trying it on, 129. If you are not careful we shall be getting complaints from people on your beat saying they are scared to let their little mongrels out in a morning in case 129 comes along and takes then away. One more thing. We don't like dogs – little ones or big ones – being kept here at Crowle Street. They bark and barking upsets the prisoners in the cells, 129. You must remember that we mustn't upset our prisoners, 129, and you must not upset me. At the moment I am getting more and more upset thinking that that little dog wants to go home and you are keeping it there against its will. Take it down Nornabell Street and let it go. If it doesn't want to go wave your truncheon in its face. It will run then I can tell you. This police station is not a dogs' home. By the way, if you have any thoughts at all for dumb animals you will get it a drink of water before you let it go, but let it go you must and do as soon as it's had a drink.' The sergeant then crashed the phone down. Graas gave the little dog a drink of water and took it into Nornabell Street where it quickly scampered away before he had time to remove the string from around its neck. Never again would he accept a found dog, no matter what the circumstances.

Later in the morning, whilst walking along Courtney Street, a middle-aged cigarette -smoking housewife with curlers in her hair and wearing a threadbare coat and slippers hurried up to him saying that there was a chimney fire in a nearby terrace at a house next to her own and that an 80-year-old lady lived there alone. Upon arrival at the house he found that the chimney had indeed been on fire but the fire in the well-polished black-leaded grate was practically out. Within a few moments the chimney smoke eased and appeared to burn itself out. There was, at his reckoning, no need for any police or fire brigade action but he advised the very pleasant but anxious old lady to have her chimney swept as soon as possible. He enjoyed a quick cup of tea with her and she told him that there was a chimney sweep living just a few houses away. She would get the job done as soon as possible, she said.

Nothing of note occurred during the remainder of the morning, but when he reported off duty at the section box he saw Sergeant Doyle and told him that he was sorry to hear about his burst tyre. He also mentioned the chimney fire. Doyle immediately asked to see his notes for summonsing the lady in respect of the fire.

'Goodness me, sergeant. The person responsible for the fire is an elderly lady – over 80-years-old, in fact. There was no way I wanted to report her. In any case the chimney fire is hardly an offence to be bothered with, is it?'

'It is not for you to decide, 129,' replied the sergeant. 'The accidental allowing of a chimney to set fire is an offence under the Town Police Clauses Act of 1847. The age of a person responsible is of no concern of yours either. Now listen, I don't normally do this, but first I am going to telephone Crowle Street and report off duty. Then, as I am in a benevolent mood I shall give you a few minutes of my own time to advise you. It will be good advice and you must not forget it.' The sergeant then telephoned Crowle Street HQ and reported off duty. On hearing Doyle's comments one constable, who was standing behind Doyle and about to commence his beat duty, put a finger up to his left temple in a screw-like fashion, as if to indicate Doyle's state of mind, then smiled wryly as he left the section box.

Doyle and Graas were left alone in the little office section box. 'Now then,' he said as he stuck his chest out with apparent pride, 'I suggest you look up the Town Police Clauses Act as soon as possible. You will have a copy in your training notes at home. You should have been taught all about it at recruit training but obviously you haven't. There are not just chimney fires to know about. You also need to know that it is an offence to fix or place any flower-pot or window-box, or other heavy article, in any upper window, without sufficiently guarding the same against being blown down into the street. Do you understand?'

'Yes, sergeant, we did hear about the Town Police Clauses Act at training,' replied Graas. 'We also discussed a commonsense approach . . .'

Doyle cut him short, 'Commonsense indeed. The application of the law does not make way for commonsense. Do 'em, that's what your job is about. Now then, where was I? Yes. It is also an offence to beat, or shake, in any street, any carpet, rug or mat – except door-mats, beaten or shaken – before the hour of eight in the morning.

There's plenty of those rag mats in this area too. Have lots of dust in them – they do. At his time of year people start putting plant pots and boxes of – pansies on window ledges without nailing them down to sufficiently guard – against the same being blown into the street. I am sure that on your beat this – morning several women shook doormats in Courtney Street near to the school. You need to keep your eyes open, lad. There are offences being committed under your nose and you seem to think these offences – and the chimney fire – is a good example – are of no concern of yours. The government did not bring these Acts of Parliament in for you to ignore them, you know. Being a Hull City policeman doesn't mean just walking about looking and feeling important. You have to let people know you are important by enforcing the law on them.'

The sergeant's flow of words continued unabated. 'I don't know why I am being a kind of father figure to you, but you have just completed your first shift by yourself. It appears to me that you have been wandering about for eight hours like a taxi without a passenger. Summonses, summonses, lad! You must get stuck in and "do" somebody for something. It's the only way to learn this job. Bicycles, motor-assisted bicycles, cars without parking lights, cars causing obstruction, dangerous parking, riding bicycles on footpaths, two people on a bicycle made for one, cars, lorries and bicycles just slowing down but not actually stopping at halt signs. Lorry drivers coming off building sites with mud all over the number plates so you can't see the registration numbers clearly are committing offences by not ensuring the numbers are clearly visible at all time. Well, stop the drivers as soon as the wheels hit the road and do 'em.'

His words now appeared to gather speed as more petty offences came to mind. 'People on bicycles making a last-second dash to get through the railway crossing gates as they are closing for an oncoming train are a good catch too. Magistrates usually give them a good fine and a rollicking. There are loads of offences to find and report, especially with all these bicycles cluttering up the roads. Stop a car and ask the driver for his licence and insurance certificate. Four times out of ten you will get an offence there too. If they haven't got the documents with them you are entitled to give them five days to produce them at a police station. That makes them realise that we policemen are the bosses. You have no excuse, 129. Do 'em. And remember, if ever you see something fall off a lorry, get the number and report the driver for having an insecure load. Just look upon your beat as something like a glorious lake full of fish and you are there doing some fishing. Catch as many as you can, but don't throw any of them back, that would be like cautioning them. Put the lot in your book and, as I have said, do 'em all.'

'Well, sergeant, you have certainly given me plenty to think about. I shall see what I can do,' replied Graas. 'But if you don't mind me saying so, I can't imagine people in Courtney Street, Buckingham Street and the like planting pansies in window-boxes, let alone planting them in such a way that they are likely to fall into the street. As far as shaking mats, carpets or whatever, well, the Town Police Clauses Act is over 100 years old and life styles have changed a lot since then.'

With his eyes piercing from beneath the peak of his helmet and his voice becoming more excited with every word, the sergeant replied, 'Listen here, 129, if there was no need for the Town Police Clauses Act the government would have revoked it, wouldn't they? Prime Ministers like Winston Churchill, Clement Attlee and Anthony Eden would not allow a law to remain in effect if it were no good. So don't you tell me that you can't imagine pansies anywhere around here. If I tell you there are pansies in window-boxes then it is up to you to find them. Apply the law, not question my authority, that's all you need to do.'

Graas sensed that Doyle was annoyed with his comment about the 100-years-old law, especially when he saw Doyle was replacing his bicycle clips to his trousers in readiness to cycle home. He had half opened the section box door as if to leave when he suddenly closed the door and said, 'And don't just think of summonses. There are plenty of arrests to be made too, you know. Drunk and incapable offenders are easy. Find someone lying flat out in the gutter and you've got an arrest for being drunk and incapable – worth a £2 fine of anybody's money. Drunk and disorderly persons, especially women, can be troublesome, mind. Women kick and scratch and spit and they often go for your goolies but generally you have the advantage because they are drunk and you are not, or shouldn't be. To prove drunkenness you only have to show that the accused is unsteady on his feet, eyes are glazed, breath smells of alcohol and the speech is slurred. You then form the opinion that the accused is drunk and you have then got him, provided, of course, that he is incapable of standing, or is disorderly, two different offences, but hardly both! I've had many a drunk in my time, especially on night. Lock a drunk up before midnight and you can be in bed by two and getting away with a full night on the streets but you have to be at court at ten o'clock, of course.'

Racing on enthusiastically, Doyle continued, 'A drunk with a bicycle is easy to a point. Just hang in the shadows near a pub late in the evening about closing time and where you can see some bicycles propped up against the wall. You don't need to prove incapable or disorderliness, just watch someone who has had a good drink and in your opinion is slightly under the influence of drink. Take hold of a bicycle and you have got him. He doesn't have to be riding it. A word of caution, mind. Try to make the arrest as near to a telephone box as you can. You see, it can be difficult getting a drunk, especially if he is flat out incapable, or you have to struggle with a drunk as well as his bicycle all the way to a telephone or section box to telephone Crowle Street for the prison van. And never ever try to blow your whistle. A prisoner will get right excited at you blowing a whistle and will most likely try to push it right down your throat. In any case no one ever seems to listen to our whistles nowadays. One more piece of advice, never run. Running often causes the helmet to fall from the head. A constable in uniform without his helmet can only be likened to a defrocked vicar.'

'I appreciate your advice, sergeant,' interrupted Graas, hoping to get away and go home.

'Yes, I feel proud to give you the benefit of my experience, 129,' replied Doyle, but much to Graas's amazement he continued, 'Remember, 129, the same criteria apply to someone driving, or merely in charge of a vehicle. If you form the opinion that the person is drunk in charge of a vehicle, let us say - as an example - some docker showing off in a little Ford Popular going home from Sutton Park Golf Club. Well, lock him up. Don't for God's sake, don't tell him to drive you to the police station as one constable did a few weeks ago. If the docker is drunk, he's drunk and surely not in a fit state to drive his car, let alone drive it when he's under arrest just to make it easy to get to the police station. Anyhow, some station sergeants will have him walk along a white line when you get him to the station but it doesn't really matter so long as you're satisfied he's drunk. If you watch outside a pub car park make sure the accused drunk has his car keys ready and is about to open the driver's door before you nick him, otherwise he will say he wasn't going to drive. Some drunks are crafty drunks, 129, so watch out. Like fish they will do their best to wriggle off the hook.'

'If a person is really drunk there shouldn't be too much of a problem, sergeant,' commented Graas.

'There are plenty of clever lawyers down Bowlalley Lane. Old Myer Wolff is really good. It is an education just to listen to him,' the sergeant replied.

Again hoping to get away home, Graas said half-heartedly, 'Thank you for your advice, Sergeant Doyle, but you make it sound as if we should be hounding the public all the time. I thought this job was as much helping people, old ladies to cross the road and that sort of thing.'

'We don't need to report people all the time, just most of the time,' came the reply. Graas viewed Doyle's advice as outrageous thinking. What a dreadful state Hull would be in if the City Police did little but persecute members of the public in the way Doyle was suggesting.

'How many people do you summons then, sergeant?' he asked.

'Don't ask what I do or don't do, 129,' replied Doyle angrily. 'I am telling you what I think you should do. Remember, 129, we would all be in trouble if the Magistrates Courts did not have any work to do. We are the providers of the work for all "their worships" and we have the Stipendiary Magistrate, Mr. O'Sullivan, who is paid a fat sum to deal with cases we give him. He would not be happy with us if we gave him no work. Now go home and dwell on what I have said. Also, I must warn you, there has been a change of duty for you. You are on the Crowle Street beat 2 pm to 10 pm tomorrow.'

'But I am on the early shift this week, sergeant,' protested Graas. 'I am taking my wife out tomorrow night.'

'You were on the early shift, now it has been changed. Don't argue about it. Constables don't argue with sergeants. You can take your wife out another night.'

'So what shift will I be on the next day, sergeant?'

'You will be back on this beat the next morning reporting here at this section box at 5.45 am.' replied Sergeant Doyle.

'So that means that I shall finish duty at 10 pm tomorrow night, cycle home and have to be back on duty in less than eight hours after that, at 5.45 am. Not much time for sleep in between, sergeant,' commented Graas.

Doyle replied, 'Your sleep is nothing to do with me, 129, unless I catch you sleeping on duty. Be off with you and tonight you can sleep on all the advice I have given you.'

As Graas cycled home he recalled that he had heard that Doyle had been quite a heavy drinker in the CID in the past but it appeared that he was now renouncing drink and attempting to use constables to persecute those who did. On Sundays when he was off duty he attended his local church where he always chose to sit in a pew right at the back of the church and in the corner where he would nod off throughout almost every sermon. There was a lot to learn about policing and even more to learn about some policemen. So ended Constable 129's first day working alone on his beat.

Another Day, Another Beat

'You are new, aren't you?' enquired a constable as he joined P.c. Graas in the Crowle Street muster room.

'Yes, I am,' Graas replied.

'Are you sure you want to be in this job? It's not all that it is cracked up to be, you know,' commented the constable as he brushed some dandruff from the shoulders of his uniform jacket. 'The discipline in this force is hellishly strict and borders on the crazy at times. I have got five years in, I should know.'

'I am new to it all,' replied Graas. 'But I hear that the Chief Constable is a bit of a terror.'

'It's not the Chief I can tell you,' the constable said. 'Take myself, for example. I am getting married in three weeks time. It's all arranged. Getting married at the Holderness Road United Reformed Church we are. It's all above board. I am not divorced or anything. My betrothed is not pregnant and it's all respectable.'

He continued, 'I cannot get my annual leave until later in the year and I accept that, so we shall have a delayed honeymoon. That's no real problem. But the wedding day is fixed for a day when I am on a week of night duty.'

'So you will be asking for a night off from one of the days of your leave allocation, won't you?' Graas enquired.

'I already have,' the constable replied. 'I put a request in writing to the Chief Inspector here at Crowle Street some time ago. I asked for the night off and made it clear that the reason was that I was getting married. He approved it but then the Superintendent heard about it a week ago. He asked to see my leave application and scribbled across my request, 'Whoever heard of anyone getting married in the middle of the night? Request refused.'

Graas laughed, and said, 'You must be kidding.'

'It's all right you laughing. I am bloody serious; getting married is no laughing matter, you know. 'Course I am not getting married in the middle of the night. The pleasure of marriage comes then, that's why the Super is refusing my request. He's never liked me, but how mean can you get? The rotten swine.'

'Well, why not go and see if you can reason with him. Surely he realises that your wedding is important?'

'I have just been to see the miserable pig. He asked me if I could read, and when I told him that that was obvious and that I wouldn't be in this job if I couldn't read, he told me to go and read his comment again because what he had written was final. He added that he could not afford to give any of his men leave when they were allocated to night duty. The evil devil also told me that there were 16 hours between the time I could go off duty at six in the morning and the time I would need to return for duty at 10 pm He said that as a wedding ceremony takes less than an hour I should have no problem fitting it in. Then in a loud voice he told me to get out of his office. What a creep! I could have cried, but if I did he would probably have me on a charge for discreditable conduct or, knowing him, he might even tell me I'm not fit to be a policeman and have me dismissed. If I could get a sick certificate I would report sick for the week. Trouble is, my GP has been invited to the wedding. Another problem is that Detective Superintendent Cocksworth lives near my future mother-in-law in Lodge Street and, if I report sick before the wedding and still have the wedding, Jim Cocksworth and everyone at Queens Gardens HQ will know about it. That would mean real trouble. Anyhow, I have decided to get on with the wedding on the day we have planned. I shall get a couple of hours sleep after I get off duty at 6 am., then have a bath and be ready for the ceremony in the afternoon. Maybe the excitement of the wedding will keep me going after that but just imagine how I will feel walking about a ruddy beat at midnight with my bride all alone in bed.'

Graas suggested that perhaps something could be worked out before the wedding day arrived.

'There is no more chance of that than the vegetables I grow on the allotment looking like the pictures on the Bees Seeds' catalogue,' replied the constable.

Later that day Graas was patrolling the Crowle Street beat that covered the streets between Craven Street to the west and Southcoates Lane, alongside Hull prison to the east. The constables knew the shift supervisory sergeant on duty that day as 'Hairy Nose'. Pc Graas had not yet met this particular sergeant but one of the other constables told Graas to be wary of him because he was very keen on making sure that constables always had their notebooks up to date. However, just as Graas walked past a telephone box at the corner of Hedon Road and Southcoates Lane, Sergeant Hairy Nose came cycling up behind him from Hedon Road. Graas recognised him immediately because he could not help noticing a half-inch tuft of hair sprouting out in an upward direction from the tip of the nose about an inch above his nostrils. Looking up at the sergeant as he pulled his bicycle brake lever to stop alongside him, Graas saw that the sergeant's eyebrows had similar tufts of hair pointing upwards, as if reaching out for sunlight from under the peak of the helmet.

'So you are 129, are you?' asked the sergeant.

'My name is Graas, sergeant, Roland Graas.'

'Don't give me that,' said the sergeant rather fiercely. 'You are 129. That's the number on your uniform. Names don't come into it. You are a number now. I will always refer to you by your number. What do you think you have a number for if it's not to identify you? Convicts and constables are known by numbers.'

Jut at that moment Hairy Nose looked up Southcoates Lane towards the railway bridge there. 'You have got yourselves a summons coming along, 129. Look up there. Now I shall see at first hand what you are made of. Get across the road and do your duty.'

Graas looked up the avenue and saw two men on a bicycle coming down the slope of the bridge towards him. He hurried across the road ready to stop the pair but as they got nearer to him they skidded to a halt and one of the men – the one who had been sitting on the bar of the bicycle – half fell off, then quickly recovered his balance and began walking alongside the other man who peddled on slowly.

Graas raised his right arm to signal the men to stop and they did so. Hairy Nose stood across the road keenly observing the incident. Much to Graas's surprise he saw that both men were wearing HMP uniforms. When asked, they gave their names, and their addresses in Southcoates Lane. Graas then said, 'I have just seen you two riding this bicycle along this road, Southcoates Lane. It is obviously a bicycle made for one. It is an offence to ride two on a bicycle. Now then, you actually riding the bicycle, what account do you give for riding this machine whilst carrying another person on the cross bar?'

'I thought it was going to rain so I was only giving my mate a ride. We was doing no harm.'

Turning to the second man, Graas said, 'What account do you give for riding on the bar of this bicycle?'

Pointing to the prison wall a few yards away, he replied, 'It's like he says. We thought it was going to rain. We are just going to work in there.'

Making his notes contemporaneously in his notebook, Graas said, 'Very well. I must inform you that you will both be reported for riding two on a bicycle. Do you understand?'

'Of course, we are prison warders, just in case you have not noticed. If that sergeant over there wasn't watching you could let us off. It seems like dog eats dog to me. You lot nick them and we keep them in for you. I thought that we were more or less in the same job,' replied the cyclist.

'As I have said, you will be reported. I am not in a position to let you off. Why don't you both get bicycles, and then there would be no problem? I don't know if you realise but you look really foolish travelling along two on the bicycle in prison officer's uniform.'

One of them replied, 'Why don't you call a bike a bike. Saying bicycle all the time is too bloody smart for these parts.'

The two warders sniggered to themselves and walked off towards the prison gates on Hedon Road. Graas walked after them until he saw them go into the prison with the bicycle.

He then checked his notes and as he was doing so the sergeant had crept up behind him and was looking over his shoulder. 'Now, 129,' he muttered, 'you didn't do badly there, but why didn't you test the bicycle brakes?'

'Come on, sergeant, 'replied Graas. 'We both saw the man riding the bicycle pull up quickly and stop. I saw that the brake blocks were nearly new and certainly not worn down. So far as I am concerned there was no need to check them.'

'All right,' replied the sergeant. 'But how do you know they haven't stolen the bicycle?'

'I did not check that aspect, sergeant,' replied Graas. 'But I did obtain their names and addresses. I did see them go into the prison. They were wearing HMP uniforms. I am satisfied that they are who they say they are. In any case I could easily identify them again.'

'What about the bicycle lights then?' enquired the sergeant.

'Goodness me, sergeant!' Graas exclaimed. 'I saw there wasn't a lamp on the lamp bracket at the front, but it's daylight, and as far as I am aware we don't report people for not having lights on their bicycles in daylight hours.'

'All right, 129. Don't get excited. Also try not to come up with silly exclamations like "goodness me". It tends to suggest that you are too damned intellectual and sensitive to be a bobby. This job is brawn as much as anything else, lad. Now let me see your notes.'

Graas dutifully handed his notebook to the sergeant. He began to read, and, half speaking to himself, said, 'Neat handwriting. Yes, it's readable, clear concise and precise. No spelling mistakes. Good. Ah, yes, you have a mistake here, 129. We don't like colloquialisms. You must never refer to a bicycle as a bike. The magistrates don't like it, your inspectors don't like it and, what's more, I don't like it. Don't let me find you using colloquialisms again. Good English is what the law is all about. A bicycle is a bicycle, not a bike. That's the kind of word the working-class use!'

Hairy Nose handed the notebook back to Graas and, as he was about to mount his bicycle Graas said, 'May I ask you a question, sergeant?'

'Yes, of course. Anything about the job and I am here to help,' he replied.

'It's not about the job, sergeant. I do hope you don't think this is too personal but, you see, I can't help wondering about the tuft of hair on the tip of your nose. I know that no one in the force is allowed to grown a beard whilst in uniform nowadays, so why isn't something done about that tuft of hair there? You must find it embarrassing.'

Hairy Nose's face suddenly bloomed into deep, almost fluorescent red as he spluttered out, 'Listen to me 12-bloody-9! I know about this damned hair. Of course, it's embarrassing. It's right here in front of me every day. If I trim it with scissors it grows back even stronger. I once had a go at shaving it, but, good God, man. It's impossible shaving your own nose – at the tip that is – can't see it right, see. Your hands get in the way of the damned mirror and you can risk lopping part of it off. I might get one of those new electric razors one day. I have seen them for sale in Hammonds. I have thought of bleaching it, but then I would run the risk of burning my skin off and having a horrible red blotch there. I have thought of all sorts, I have. It doesn't help one little bit with the likes of you bringing it up like you are doing. Your impertinence does you no good at all, you know. That's the trouble with young policemen nowadays. In the old days, no one would ever dare to ask such a damn fool personal question and I trust that you will never have the audacity to ask such a question again.'

'Yes, sergeant, but I am sympathetic and I am sorry I asked you,' replied Graas.

'OK,' said Hairy Nose, obviously in a state of embarrassment. 'At least you are open about it, not like them at Crowle Street who talk about it behind my back.' Then as he was about to ride away he said, 'Don't ever let me catch you describing a bicycle as a bike again, and, by the way, the word tuft is for describing grass not human hair.'

He then rode off towards Alexandra Dock, narrowly escaping the wheels of a Bedford lorry as it came thundering towards him from the direction of Marfleet.

Teddy Boys and Cockroaches

Inspector Charles McWhoo came pedalling along Cleveland Street on his old but well polished Hercules bicycle one Friday afternoon. Pc Graas recalled that other constables told him to be on his guard when Inspector McWhoo was around as he was apparently obsessed with efficiency and that he would go into a rage should he find anything untoward with any constable's beat work. He was also a well-decorated World War Two veteran and thought to be quite prosperous. He had just become the owner of a grey Morris Minor Traveller with an AA badge on the front!

As the Inspector approached Graas gave him a smart salute, but, just as his right hand completed the salute, a number 32 Hull Corporation bus from Sutton went by hurriedly. 'Were you saluting me or the bus driver,' demanded the Inspector angrily.

'Y-you, sir,' replied Graas nervously

'Then give me eye to eye contact when you express your respect for me with your salute in future,' said the Inspector as he alighted from his bicycle. 'So, you are 129, are you?'

Trying hard to rid himself of being known by his number, Graas replied, 'Actually, my name is Roland Graas, sir.'

'Actually, actually nothing!' the Inspector thundered. 'One of the sergeants told me that you tried it on him, wanting to be called by your name. You don't expect to be called by the name your mother gave you, do you? How you have the audacity to even hint that I call you by your name I don't know. Listen, and listen real well. You are 129. Your name is no concern of mine. I can't go writing names in my notebook of constables I have seen on beats. Numbers is what it is all about, it's more efficient. What if we had a lot of Smiths? How would we manage then? Names are for officers like me, and, of course, sergeants supervising you all. Constables are numbers. Now I want your notebook.'

Graas took his notebook from his breast pocket, opened it at the last entry and handed it to the Inspector. Looking at it he said, 'Yes, you have it right up to date, 129. That is what I like to see. Notebooks kept up to date and neatly written is all part of being an efficient policeman. I shall sign it to say that I have examined it. But tell me, 129, how did you come to be posted to east Hull? It is usually policemen who have been in a bit of trouble, or who have upset someone, who get posted to this division.'

'I don't think I have upset anyone, sir, 'replied Graas. 'And I don't know why I was posted here.'

Becoming friendlier by the second he said, 'Well, maybe the powers-that-be at Queens Gardens have sent you here to kind of throw you in at the deep end. It's tough working in east Hull. We have tough, stand-for-no-nonsense senior officers here. If you succeed your two years' probationary period here you will manage most anything this job will throw at you. You won't know this, 129, but this force was not very efficient ten years ago. Then Chief Constable Sidney Lawrence was appointed. God, what a difference he has made. The force needed it, mind. The new superintendents are on their toes all the time and everything is done as it should be done. Lawrence certainly made many officers sit up. Many do not like him, but this force was in need of discipline before he arrived and he has certainly provided it. He sent senior officers a memo a while back stressing the need for discipline and punishment. It is a masterpiece of instruction. It is addressed to inspectors and above but I shall let you see it. You see you are new to police work and weighing you up – I have read your personal file – I reckon you should get on in this job. Appreciating the memo will be worth your while in the years to come. Always take notice of my advice, 129. I feel that I can be a father figure to you!'

'Thank you, sir,' replied Graas, 'but you have only just met me.'

The Inspector replied, 'I examined your note book just now, I have examined your personal file, and with my experience of life I can tell you now that I am a good judge of character. I have noted that you took a drop in your pay from £12 to £9 a week coming into the force. And I don't expect you had to work nights and most weekends in the RAF, did you? Not like the police. Shows that you must be keen to be a policeman. Coming to join the Hull force when you and your wife don't know anyone here is another credit to you. Good to see you.'

Taken aback by the generosity of his comments Graas did not know what to say. Inspector McWhoo mounted his bicycle, eyeballs-to-eyeball salutes were exchanged, and the Inspector whistled an unidentifiable tune to himself as he rode away. It appeared to Graas that McWhoo derived some pleasure from his change of attitude but he was quietly suspicious of the Inspector's apparent friendliness, So ended Graas's first, and, when all was said and done, quite pleasing encounter with Inspector McWhoo. Graas continued his late afternoon patrol along Cleveland Street towards Witham. As he approached the Jennings Street junction he saw a middle-aged man riding a bicycle towards him along Jennings Street and then across the Cleveland Street junction without stopping. There was a 'Major Road Ahead' signpost in Jennings Street prior to the junction. There was very little other traffic there at the time. Nevertheless, as the cyclist approached, Graas raised his right hand and gave the signal to stop. The cyclist cheekily rode up to within an inch or so of Graas's boots and then gently, but deliberately, pushed the front wheel against one of the boots, rubbing mud off the tyre onto the polished toecap of the boot. Graas was about to caution the man for the traffic sign infringement but glancing at his boot he chose to say nothing about it but, instead, he changed his mind about a caution. He pointed to the 'Halt' sign, and said, 'I saw you cycling past the halt sign there in Jennings Street and then ride across

Cleveland Street without stopping. What account do you give for failing to comply with the halt sign?'

Clearly annoyed, the cyclist replied, 'There should be a better white line across the road than there is as well as the halt sign. Can't you see that my bike's fitted with drop handlebars? How am I expected to be looking up at halt signs on the side of the street, hold on to the drop handlebars that automatically make me look down, and for that matter also keep an eye open for damned young coppers like you at the same time?'

Taking another glance at the scuff of mud on his boot, Graas obtained the man's name and address and continued, 'I am reporting you for failing to comply with the halt sign. Do you understand?'

'Understand, understand, 'course I bloody understand,' said the cyclist. 'Do you take me for an imbecile or something? No I had better not say imbecile. Coppers can't spell big words, can they? No, I will re-phrase it. Do you take me for a fool? That's better. It is spelt f-o-o-l. Anyway, I know you lot. Get a damned summons in your book and keep it there for a rainy day. When it's raining you can never see a copper anywhere because they are all inside in the dry writing out summons reports. Doing poor bloody cyclists so that you have got one up your sleeve to avoid getting wet is a right rotten way of going on, that's all. Plain rotten lot you are.'

He cycled off, but, when he was about 100 yards away, he turned back and rode up to Graas again saying, 'You should come to work at Paul's Mill, then you would know what a day's work is.'

'You know that 20 people were killed in road accidents in Hull last year. Riding a bicycle out of a side street and straight across a major road like you did could cause a nasty accident,' replied Graas.

'You know what? You sound like that copper Dixon on TV who thinks that he is God's gift to mankind,' he said. 'Bet you can't afford a television, can you? Anyway I'm going home. I don't have to stop here talking to you. You'll still be walking about these grotty streets later on when I am at home with missus and my TV laughing at Tony Hancock. I shall be thinking about you then and have a quiet chuckle to myself. If you can't spell, get yourself back to Jennings Street, at least there you can copy the words on the sign "Major Road Ahead".' He shook his head mockingly, laughed to himself and rode off again.

Shortly afterwards Sergeant Hairy Nose cycled up to Graas. 'Walking along feeling important again are we, 129? Inspector Knight is on this shift today. He knows a malingerer when he sees one, so watch out. You should have got yourself a summons or two up there in Jennings Street by now. Look, I will show you. Come with me. I will show you where to hide in a doorway and have a good view of the cyclists nipping past the junction without stopping. It's like catching bees around a pot of jam there. Easy offence to prove too.'

'But if I just stood there without hiding, then by being there where people would see me I could prevent people nipping past the junction without stopping,' answered Graas.

'Catch 'em at it, that's best, sting the pocket, that keeps people law abiding, 129,' replied the sergeant.

'I have just caught a man who will be reported for failing to comply with the halt sign, sergeant.'

'Oh, why didn't you say so? Getting down to the job, are you? That's pleasing. Right, let me see your notebook. It is all part of my duty to check summons notes,' replied Hairy Nose.

He then examined the notebook and said, 'He's a cheeky devil, this one. Wish we could summons people like him who think we can't spell. Insulting, that's what it is. I'd give him imbecile if I caught him. Did you show him that you could spell it correctly? And to think that me and Inspector McWhoo fought for people like him in the war.'

'I would think he was fighting in the war too, sergeant. You will see by notes that he is 41-years-old,' commented Graas.

'Ah, well, that's as maybe,' replied the sergeant. 'Now listen. I want you to make your way to Holderness Road section box for nine o'clock tonight. We're having trouble with Teddy Boys loitering about shop doorways between Craven Street and Boddy's Funeral Parlour beside Jalland Street in the late evenings and making a nuisance. You will meet another constable at the section box. I want the two of you to clear the Teds away. Call it obstruction of the pavement, conduct likely to cause a breach of the peace, call it whatever you like. Get them out and away from the shop doorways, that's what I want. Some may have been drinking, mind. The Elephant and Castle is nearby, remember, and the Nags Head, corner of Waller Street. Some Teds like a good drink, usually Hull bitter, makes then think they are grown men, it does. Remember; don't stand any lip from them. If they use obscene language, that is the F or the C word, lock 'em up. Using swear words like that in public is an offence and you have power to arrest for it.'

'Yes, sergeant,' replied Graas, 'but you know we can hardly say that people standing in doorways are obstructing the pavement, can we? Shop doorways are not part of the pavement, are they? And all the shops are closed well before 9 pm.'

'They won't have told you about the Ways and Means Act at police training school, 129. It is an Act of Parliament that MPs have in their hearts but cannot get through the Commons. However, the trouble with instructors at police training is that they have never done the practical side of the job. Don't worry. I will see to it that you have an experienced constable with you. And remember this. I don't want you being assaulted by the Teds. If one of my men is assaulted I look upon him as failing in his duty. Bringing assault police charges against members of the public, even Teddy Boys, is a sign of failure in the proper police approach. Don't forget that.'

'Can I just mention the obscene language charge you have spoken of? I thought we had to show that someone was annoyed or embarrassed by the use of the actual words. Is that right?' asked Graas.

'Yes, fair comment, 129,' replied the sergeant. 'All you have to do is look around when you have heard the offending word, word or words, notice that some woman look annoyed or upset on hearing the words and you have got the full offence. It's simple.'

'What if there is no one around looking upset or annoyed, sergeant?'

'The Ways and Means Act will always make it look as if there is, lad. We can't have yobs thinking that they can get away with using obscene and bad language in public, can we? You see it's easy. Most women have an annoyed look just waiting for a bus or carrying a shopping bag. How are you to know what they are annoyed about? All you have to say in your evidence is that a woman looked annoyed.' He smiled as he added, 'My missus is a good example. She always looks annoyed about something. Anyhow, use your imagination, 129, that's what the Ways and Means Act is all about. It is also the oil that keeps law and order in the streets of this grand country of ours.'

About nine o'clock that evening Pc Graas met the tall and solid former Royal Navy petty officer, Pc Bold, at the Holderness Road section box. 'I have been told you are with me to learn a few tricks of the trade,' he said. 'What's your name?'

'I'm Roland Graas,' he replied.

'Can't be bothered with numbers, me,' replied Bold. 'You know, if you are thinking that you are going into a bit of a fracas somewhere, usually a domestic disturbance, it's not a bad idea to stand in a quiet corner and change your number about a bit. Yours is 129. Just clip out the nine and swop it with the one. Then it will be 921. Our numbers don't go as far as that. You see, should you have to go into a fracas a bit heavy and they don't like it and complain, they will obviously get your number wrong. Once they do that their complaint will already be on difficult ground. If they appear to make a mistake about your number, how reliable can they be with the rest of their complaint? We have got to look after ourselves in this business. Remember, though, never forget to change your number back as soon as you can after the fracas, otherwise someone like old Hairy Nose will have a fit and you will be on a discipline charge.'

'You are not kidding, are you?' asked Graas.

'Maybe I am. Protection of the public they say. Well there is also protection of the police to think about Roland. We need to protect ourselves too you know. If we don't, no one else will,' replied the confident avuncular and experienced Pc Bold.

'I can't imagine there would ever be time to change the numbers when you are on your way to attend a spot of trouble,' replied Graas.

'If there is a fracas, a quarrel, a fight, call it what you will, then don't rush, Roland. Let them bash hell out of themselves first. That way they are usually breathless by the time you get there and they are easier to deal with. I reckon with you not being the biggest of coppers you could be inviting them to have a go at you by your size alone. Protect yourself by not being there when the boot comes in. It's no good being a hero lying on your back in the Infirmary.'

'Thanks. I appreciate your advice,' commented Graas.

'Well now, Roland, do you think you are up to it? It could be a bit rough tonight. There is talk of Hull Brewery putting the price of a pint up a penny tomorrow so some idiots will be drinking a bit more than usual tonight.'

'Yes, I am ready. I wouldn't have joined the police if I weren't ready for any eventuality,' replied Graas.

'We don't have big words like eventuality in this job, lad,' said Bold earnestly. 'Use simple words all the time, then when you nick someone they understand what you are saying. Simple words make it easy for you in the witness box as well. Damned solicitors try to outwit us when we use long words. The cheeky baskets try to make out we don't know the meaning of long words. I know, but I usually beat them at their own game. Commonsense is all that this job needs.'

'Yes. I see what you mean,' replied Graas rather patronisingly.

'Now tonight we are going to protect life and property,' said Bold. 'Shops are vulnerable property and so we have to check that shop doors are properly locked. If they are insecure the Teds will be in and they will nick anything. Come with me. We shall walk side by side and I shall do the door checking. You can just watch.'

Graas saw Bold was carrying a pair of white cotton gloves in his right hand. 'Oh, I haven't got any gloves with me,' he exclaimed. 'Do I need gloves for anything?'

'No. I just carry them. It's a habit with me, that's all,' replied Bold.

They both walked along Holderness Road side by side. Pc Bold's long legs allowed him to stride forth at the pace of a grandfather clock whilst Graas's little legs gave him a pace more in keeping with the tick of a pocket watch. Feeling embarrassed, he tried hard to keep pace with Bold but gave up within a minute or so. Within a few minutes they saw two Teddy Boys standing inside a shop doorway at the corner of Holderness Road and Nornabell Street. Pc Bold quickly walked into the doorway and behind the youths, leaving Graas standing a few yards away. Without uttering a word Bold quickly flicked his gloves behind the ears of one of the youths, one after the other in quick succession. This caused them both to dash out of the doorway, covering their ears with their hands and at the same time cursing Pc Bold. Then, with no more ado, they hurried away across the road and disappeared into Craven Street.

'That was quite remarkable,' said Graas as they continued their patrol along the pavement.

'Comes with experience,' replied Bold nonchalantly.

The two constables continued along Holderness Road as several Teddy Boys begrudgingly moved on as they approached. Nearing Buckingham Street they saw eight Teddy Boys congregating in and around Boots Chemist's shop-door. Without a word from anyone Pc Bold swiftly walked into the shop entrance and behind the group, followed this time by the slightly more apprehensive Pc Graas. Bold had hardly tried the shop-door lock when, once again, he appeared to wave his gloves behind the Teddy Boys' heads. Like lightning they all stumbled and part dashed across the pavement, some holding the backs of their heads as if the cotton gloves flicking had caused them some pain.

As they dashed away, one of them yelled, 'Come on, we aren't doing any harm. Just 'cause we got D.A. haircuts, crew cuts and flash drainpipes you bobbies treat us like scum. Why can't you leave us alone?' Then he added, 'I bet old Hairy Nose has told you to move us on. It's only when he's around that we get this aggro.'

Pc Bold stood still in front of the now empty shop doorway. He said nothing but stared menacingly at the group. Graas decided to stare at them just as threateningly but didn't feel they were as concerned about him as they were with his glove-waving colleague. After a few seconds the group wandered off across Holderness Road and then into a side-street terrace of houses in Sherburn Street.

'That one with the purple jacket, yellow shirt, boot-lace tie and ginger hair lives down there,' said Bold. 'He can be right cheeky at times. Sometimes carries a sheath knife too. I warned his dad about it some time ago. Haven't noticed the knife since. His dad works at Reckitt's. Good man he is too.'

'I can't help but notice that you don't speak to them at all and that they appear to ignore you until you are right behind them flicking your gloves,' commented Graas.

'Yes. You see, if I tell them to move they will just as likely say that I threatened them. In any case I don't believe in wasting my breath on Teds. Actions speak louder than words in this job, you know,' replied Bold.

Walking across Holderness Road they saw three more Teddy Boys inside one of Woolworth's shop doorways. As the constables approached the three youths swiftly moved out of the doorway laughing. 'You aren't getting us with your kid glove treatment, Mr. Bold! And don't go teaching this new bobby any of your tricks. Swinging his gloves with that helmet on will have him overbalancing.'

Bold glared at the three but said nothing. They apparently sensed his annoyance and walked away, chattering among themselves.

Bold's methods bore no relation whatsoever to all that Graas was taught at the training school but the flicking of the gloves fascinated him. 'Can I see your gloves for a moment?' he asked Bold.

'Gloves. They're just police issue gloves, nothing special about them,' said Bold. 'What do you want to see them for?'

'They seem a bit special to me,' said Graas. 'The way those Teddy Boys move gives me the impression the gloves must have some kind of electric current in them somewhere. It can't be just the flick of the glove that gets them moving as they do.'

'You heard one of them say I was giving them the kid glove treatment, didn't you? Well, giving them the kid glove treatment means that I am being soft and not doing them any harm, doesn't it?' replied Bold.

'Yes, I guess it does,' replied Graas thoughtfully.

'But you want to see my gloves. You can see them, but let's get into Woolworth's shop doorway first,' said Bold.

Once they were in the doorway Bold handed the pair of gloves to Graas who, on examining them, was amazed to find that there were what appeared to be a marble sown into each of two of the fingertips of the gloves. 'Wow!' he exclaimed. You have two little marbles hidden in each glove. No wonder they get out of your way. You know you are assaulting them with these and could be in serious trouble for that.'

'Yes, but you must agree its marbleous kid glove treatment too. But take a closer look. They are not marbles. I tried clay marbles once but they broke up on impact with some nut case,' said Bold. 'If you have a good look you will see I have perfected it now. Ball bearings is what is in there now.'

Graas handed the gloves back to Bold. 'Come on,' said Bold. 'I'll show you something down Newbridge Road. Hairy Nose has had to go to Crowle Street and I know that the inspector is up on Longhill Estate so we have got time to get a rogue or two.'

Graas was rather concerned about leaving the Holderness Road patrol but he was inquisitive too and agreed to Bold's invitation to go to Newbridge Road. In any case it was only a few hundred yards away and he thought it best not to ask what Bold was about to do there. So off they went along Sherburn Street, across Newbridge Road and then into a side passage near a bakery.

'Now stand perfectly still. Back against the wall,' said Bold. 'Glancing down at Graas's boots he added, 'Trouble is you don't have quiet enough soles and heels on those boots of yours. Take a tip from me, Roland. Get some rubber soles and heels. It will pay you dividends in this work. Soft rubber soles on your boots helps catch villains much better than metal studs. Try running along these streets with studs in your boots and you will be on your backside in no time. Anyhow, we shall now stand in this passage perfectly still. There will be movement here sooner than you think. And get your truncheon out and hold it firmly beside you. Now, got it. Good. Don't move and don't speak. Just watch me. I shall use mine first, then if necessary you can use yours!'

With a surge of excitement building up inside, Graas whispered. 'What's going to happen . . . ?'

But through gritted teeth Bold said, 'Just shut up. I have told you once. Shut up and keep your back to the wall, keep your eyes wide open and watch me going into action.'

Standing there in the shadows, Graas was concerned about the situation he found himself in. As the minutes ticked by, he worried about being off his beat on Holderness Road and what he had witnessed with the ball-bearing gloves. It was all right for Bold; he had long since completed his probation. But then, although Bold was saying very little, there did appear to be a chance of a good arrest in the offing, and then the superintendent might praise them. Bold must have good information from somewhere. With truncheons at the ready it did seem that some exciting police work was about to happen. Graas also thought of the training advice regarding the use of the truncheon and, glancing towards the end of the narrow passage, he saw that there was a door which that appeared to lead into the bakery. Perhaps Bold knew that there was going to be a robbery and the robbers were going to make their getaway through the door. Graas had already been told to shut up once, so he dare not ask any more questions. Looking around further, he saw that there was a manhole cover a few yards along the passage. In his naivety he thought that maybe someone was going to appear from under the manhole. He recalled that it was only a few weeks ago that he had seen a film at the Regal in Ferensway where some bank robbers had made their getaway from a bank robbery by using a sewer.

The passage was shadowy and partly lit by a nearby street lamp. It was no more than a little over a shoulder width with brick walls on both sides. Graas began to think that there would be little room to swing his truncheon, especially if he was to try to do it in the Home Office approved style by aiming at the shoulders. But Pc Bold was well respected and an experienced constable who had been giving evidence in a not guilty case at Hull Quarter Sessions only the week before. The judge in the case had even commended him for his powers of observation! Weighing up the present situation, Graas decided to do as he was told. Stand perfectly still, be quiet and wait.

He stood alongside Bold for several more minutes, gripping hold of the truncheon and not even daring to whisper or move his feet in case he crunched some gravel under his boots. Was the bakery door going to burst open with some robber attempting a getaway? With his heart racing he also thought that there must be some violence to come. What was the need to be at the ready with truncheons drawn if there wasn't the chance of violence? Standing there full of trepidation Graas recalled a constable once telling him never to draw his truncheon because there was always the chance that a villain would take it off him and whack him over the head with it – helmet or no helmet. No matter what was going to happen now he decided that no one was going to grab his truncheon so he quietly wrapped the truncheon strap tight around his wrist and held on to it as if his life depended on it.

Keeping his eyes open for any signs of movement, he saw Pc Bold suddenly hold his truncheon in a vertical position about six inches out in front of his chest. Then, holding it at the top end in his right hand and at the same time looking down at the ground he let go of the truncheon. It hit the ground, bottom end first with a deep sounding ping and shot back up in the air to waist height as Bold grabbed hold of it again. With a highly satisfied expression on his face he smiled and said, 'Got one, best use a truncheon can ever have. See how it's done?'

'Done, done what?' asked the bewildered Graas.

'Protecting the public. Comes under the Public Health Act it does. Look down there. You can get one if you are quick and have a good aim,' said Bold.

'Get one? Get one what?' exclaimed Graas.

'Where are your powers of observation, Roland, my lad? Can't you see it?' asked Bold. 'There will be another one soon. Shiny black germ carriers, that's what they are. I hate damned cockroaches. Can't you see that one I have just squashed into the ground? Just one direct hit and it's all smashed to pulp. Cockroaches can always be found near a bakery – now there is one less. You can only get them at night. Now you can have a go in a minute. One will come out to see what's happened to his mate. Good aim is essential, mind. They can run fast and they only come out when it's dark. Dead before they know it with my method.'

'Why cockroaches?' whispered Graas, still standing in the ready position with his truncheon still clasped tight.

'I've studied them, I have,' whispered Bold. 'There are several different types. There is the small German cockroach, he's yellowish and comes off German ships in the docks. Then there is the American species, he's brown and almost twice as long as the German brute. Reckon the Yanks left him behind after the war. Then there is the British cockroach, he's black, doesn't know why, but he's not quite as big as the American specimen. The black ones, most don't have wings, you know. God only knows why, but they can run right fast. Funny, isn't it. Of course, there are some I reckon have cross- bred with the American and German breeds. They all eat all sorts of food. The mess and smell they leave behind spoils food they run over. They seem to like bakeries. I'll tell you this in confidence. Old Hairy Nose gave me a right telling off once when he saw that the rear light on my bike was not working. It was right beside a bus stop queue and him telling me off there annoyed me. Anyway, the next night I caught me a real hungry looking cockroach and slipped it into his sandwich tin. Down at Crowle Street later that night he ate his sandwiches. I reckon the cockroach was hiding, or sleeping, in one of his cheese sandwiches. He ate the lot.'

At that moment Sergeant Hairy Nose went cycling by the top of the passage but he didn't see Bold and Graas there. Pc Bold saw him, though, and said quietly, 'Hold on a minute, Roland. We had better get back to Holderness Road. I've just seen Hairy Nose ride by on that old bike of his. You can try your own cockroach bashing – under the Public Health Act – if you are on this beat at night sometime. Another bit of Public Health Act work can be done on Stoneferry Road, you know. If you are down there near Lorraine Street when it's dark and quiet in the early hours of the morning, look out. There is nothing much that moves about there about three to four in the morning. It's really quiet. You can take a bit of bread and just put it in the gutter off the pavement edge. Stand very still – rubber soles and heels, remember – and wait for about five minutes with your truncheon out of sight but up your sleeve and you are bound to see a rat come creeping along the gutter. Then, just when he's nibbling away at the bread, you can, if you're quick, whack him across the back and kill him. Rats are vermin, that's all they are.'

Bold continued, 'Now we had better get back to Holderness road. We've given it a couple of minutes before we go because Hairy Nose is a crafty old rascal. He sometimes doubles back on himself on that bike of his trying to catch constables out taking short cuts on the fixed beat routes. But if he does see us before we get to the main road I shall tell him we've been following some Teds as we thought they might be causing some trouble. Don't ever tell him about the cockroach thing. He would think that bombing cockroaches is not police duty.'

Graas at last got a word in, 'What you have just said about Stoneferry Road rats is a bit odd to say the least. Why do you say keep the truncheon up your sleeve? Surely if a rat knows you are there he won't come along to eat the bread anyway and hiding the truncheon out of a rat's sight really doesn't make sense.'

'No, no,' replied Bold. 'It's not a case of hiding it from a rat, Roland. Keeping it out of sight in case Hairy Nose comes along is what I mean. If he sees you with your truncheon drawn – especially at three in the morning – he would think there was going to be a riot or, most likely, he would think that you were frightened of being on your own in the dark.'

Cycling home later that night, Graas felt that working with Pc Bold was indeed a curious and challenging experience and, no, he would not have ball bearings sewed into his gloves. Someone could grab the gloves and whack him with them instead.

The Inquisitive Inspector

It was a fairly quiet and pleasantly warm Sunday afternoon on Holderness Road as Pc Graas patrolled past the East Hull library. He was on his way to a house in Dansom Lane to attend to a complaint about a dangerous dog. As he looked ahead he saw Inspector McWhoo sitting in the only police car Eastern Division had – a black Ford Prefect. It was parked facing east on Holderness Road a few yards east of the Wilton Street traffic lights.

As Graas approached, the Inspector got out of the vehicle. 'Good afternoon, sir,' said Graas as he gave the Inspector a salute. With a warm and friendly smile the Inspector returned the salute and said, 'Now then, 129. How are you this afternoon?'

Appreciating the apparent friendliness of the occasion, Graas smiled and said, 'I am fine, sir. I am on my way to Dansom Lane to see someone about a complaint I have received of a dangerous dog.'

'Then I shall come with you. I want to talk to you when you have attended to the dog complaint,' said McWhoo. 'Jump in the car. It will save your legs a bit.'

Graas found the Inspector's rather patronising attitude embarrassing

but, joining with the mood of the moment, he got in the car with the Inspector, saying, 'Thank you, sir. It's good to see you have the use of the car today. I don't think it is right that you should have to ride your bicycle all the time, especially when it's windy and raining.'

'It is nice of you to think of me like that, 129. No one usually needs the car on a Sunday afternoon. The Superintendent and Chief Inspector are both off duty on Sundays and today I am responsible for the division.' Lowering his voice the Inspector continued, 'Anyway, it is handy having the car this afternoon as I want to speak to you in confidence.'

He now sounded serious but still friendly – maybe for a reason – and this made Graas feel uneasy. Has he found out about the cockroach killing, or, worse still, the kid glove treatment? There was one thing for certain: Graas was not going to grass on anyone.

Taking the bull by the horns he asked, 'What do you want to talk about, sir? I am getting along all right with my probation, aren't I?'

'Good gracious, of course you are,' answered the Inspector. 'Don't you fret about that, 129. You are doing fine, but you have quite some time to go yet before you are a fully-fledged constable. Just keep up the good work, that's all.'

Graas could not find anyone at the house when he called to enquire about the dangerous dog so he decided to call again some other time. As he left, a neighbour shouted to him, 'They have all gone to Withernsea for the day. They will be drinking too much and will get the last train back tonight.'

'Thank you,' said Graas. 'I shall call again tomorrow.'

He returned to the car and the Inspector beckoned him inside. 'Sit down, 129. No one in, I see. Never mind, you can call and see them later,' he said. 'You have been in this division long enough now to know much of what is going on among the men on your shift, haven't you? All the men know you and, of course, by now you know them. Many are good former war service men, but nowadays there are some like you who have not seen war service. They are young, bright, intelligent and ready to make a good career in the police service. In fact, I look to men of your calibre to rise to high rank, 129. And rightly so. Loyalty to one's superiors is of paramount importance in the business of furthering one's career. I am sure you appreciate that.'

Feeling uneasy by McWhoo's comments, Graas asked, 'Is this what you wanted to talk to me about, sir?'

'No, not exactly,' he replied. 'But I do want you to know that, as I am your inspector, you must always feel free to tell me anything that's going on in the division. What I mean is anything that especially affects the other constables – gossip, problems the men may have, any associations that may have with women, especially with women of the night, if you know what I mean?'

At least he's not fishing for cockroach killing or ball bearings in secret places, thought Graas as he tried to understand what the Inspector was after. 'Do you want me to tell tales, sir?' he asked innocently.

'I don't like it being put that way, 129, but yes. To put it bluntly I do need to know certain things,' he replied.

'But I don't know the other constables well enough to know anything much about them,' said Graas. 'As you know we are not allowed to gossip on our beats. In any case I'm nearly always working on a beat by myself and I rarely see anyone on an adjacent beat. At meal break times the breaks are so staggered that there is rarely a time when two constables are in the section box eating their sandwiches and drinking tea at the same time. On top of that, it's not in my nature to tell tales, sir.'

'That is all very well, but I have a specific question for you. It is very important that I get the honest answer I expect you to give. I don't consider it telling tales either and what you tell me will not be put down to you.'

'I am honest, sir, but if I don't know I can't tell you, can I?' asked Graas. But being fascinated by the approach, he leaned towards the Inspector and, with a hand mockingly covering his mouth, he asked, 'But what do you want to know, Inspector?'

Inspector McWhoo immediately grabbed Graas firmly by the arm and said, 'A constable on this shift has got VD. I must discover who it is.'

As he released his grip on Graas's arm, Graas replied, 'Wow, Inspector. It's not me. I learned all about venereal disease in the RAF. It scared me stiff just thinking about it. Honest, it's not me. Golly, you don't think I have been out with what you describe as one of the women of the night, do you?'

'No, 129. I don't think it is you for one moment,' replied McWhoo.

'Whatever prompts you to think someone has got VD on the shift and that I should know who it is?' asked Graas.

'I have my nose to the ground, 129. Inspectors have to. I have heard it said that one of the constables is referred to quietly as VD and, as no one in the division has the initials VD, I aim to find out who has obviously got VD and I have decided that you are the one to help me,' said McWhoo.

'Why me, sir?' demanded Graas.

'The men close ranks when they know that I want to find out about something of a discipline nature. You are new and not fully in with the clique yet. Anyhow, you are pretty observant, very keen to get on and from what I have seen you are a real nosey young copper. Someone has definitely got VD, 129. I shall, with your help, find out who it is,' stated McWhoo confidently.

'If you think I am going to sneak into the toilet at the section box, Crowle Street, or wherever, in the belief that I can spot some unfortunate policeman with scabs around his penis you have another thought coming,

Inspector. Find someone else or check at the VD clinic, Mr. McWhoo, but leave me out of it,' said Graas sternly.

'The VD clinic won't ever say anything,' replied McWhoo.

'Do you really think that some constable on this shift has been foolish enough to associate with one of the prostitutes who prance about the pavements and use the all-night cafés opposite Alexandra Dock, sir?' asked Graas.

'Well now, 129, you have let it slip, haven't you. You've known all the time, haven't you? Now tell me who it is? Come on, 129. You must tell me, that's an order,' said McWhoo.

'Good gracious, sir, I don't know, honest,' replied Graas.

'Then why mention the women at the Hedon Road cafés prancing about the pavement,' demanded McWhoo.

'That's the only place I have actually seen any prostitutes in the division who are possibly suffering from venereal disease, sir,' replied Graas.

'Prostitutes prancing on the pavement,' commented the Inspector thoughtfully. 'Not against the law in itself, 129, but use the phrase next time you arrest a common prostitute, Graas. The magistrates will love the phrase. It will have them appreciate how well we can describe the antics of the miscreants we have to deal with. Now then, appreciating that I believe you have a good future, I have copied the memo I told you about a few days ago. The one where the Chief Constable has given splendid instructions – in writing –about enforcing good discipline and management. I was going to give you a copy for your future reference, but I shall hold on to it for now. You can have it when you can tell me who the man is who has got VD. Now you can go. A walk down the section box will give you time to think about loyalty and your future in this job.'

Graas said nothing but got out of the Inspector's car, deliberately failed to salute him and walked away. 'Why in heaven's name ask me?' Graas mused. It was a kind of blackmail treating a probationary constable like this, but VD was serious. He recalled seeing a film about it when he joined the RAF, but, apart from one aircraftsman 2nd class being scared of catching the disease after an affair with a girl he met at Liverpool's Lime Street station, the subject had not been mentioned anywhere since. Not even at the police training school. Inspector McWhoo obviously believed that someone actually on the shift had got the dreaded disease and he thought that Graas knew, or could discover, the culprit. But surely no one in the force – let alone his shift – could possibly be so foolish, or could they? After all, policemen are recruited from the human race!

Inspector McWhoo was an experienced officer and appeared to know what he was talking about. Why was he putting pressure on young Graas, though? And using the somewhat insecure existence of the constable's probationary time in order to find out what he wanted.

Several days followed, but whenever McWhoo saw Graas he never mentioned the VD problem to him. Nevertheless, it was always in the back of Graas's mind and the occasional light-hearted comment from the Inspector made Graas realise that McWhoo had not forgotten it either.

One day a Hull Corporation Transport tower wagon drove under the railway bridge at the junction of Holderness Road and Craven Street and jammed under the bridge because the tower part of the vehicle had not been fully lowered. Graas reported the driver for careless driving. Inspector McWhoo checked the summons report and, having found it in order, he said, 'When you have done your best, you should await the result in peace, Graas.'

Graas took the remark to have a meaning far and above the careless driving summons of the Corporation tower wagon driver. More to the point it meant, 'Tell me who has got VD and you can await the completion of your probation in peace!'

He had now been in Hull getting on for a year. The policemen he had met were generally fair, friendly and good at their work but rarely smiled at anything. It was as if they had to be serious about everything all the time. Maybe the smiling Dixon of Dock Green character he remembered from watching TV in Ireland was, sadly, just an entertainment figure. For instance, Dixon did not appear to summons anyone, but in Hull's Eastern Division it was almost the order of the day, with constables being hounded by their sergeants and inspectors if a month went by without a constable summonsing someone for something.

With Inspector McWhoo's demand to identify the VD carrier and his veiled threat about the probation situation forever in the back of his mind, Graas took the bull by the horns one day at Crowle Street. He asked one of the middle-aged constables there if he knew of anyone who had VD in the division. 'My God, what a question! Are you serious? What the hell are you saying?' The normally mild and gentle constable exploded. 'You are hinting that someone in the force has got VD. You had better be careful, my lad. Defamation, that's what it is. You had better be careful what you are saying. What if anyone's wife got to hear such a thing? If the Chief gets to hear such a thing then heaven help us all. No, I don't know of anyone who has got V bloody D. I can tell you this, though. I bet the whole of my pension that no one has. Whatever makes you ask? Where did you hear such a thing? You will be in deep trouble talking like this, lad. Don't ever think such tripe again.'

Graas certainly did not want to say that he had had his confidential chat with Inspector McWhoo, so he replied that he had picked it all up in canteen gossip.

'That's a laugh,' commented the constable as he calmed down. 'It won't be canteen gossip in this division will it? We haven't got a canteen here, have we?'

'No, we haven't,' replied Graas sheepishly. 'Maybe it came from Central Division in Queens Gardens.

'Then don't repeat dangerous bloody gossip, lad. Remember you could be in trouble for that. Inspector McWhoo would be down your throat like a double dose of syrup of figs if he heard you talk like that,' advised the constable.

'Sorry,' muttered Graas as he began to study a variety of crime reports and stolen vehicle circulations.

Two nights later he found himself working with the ball bearing gloved constable on Holderness Road once more. After clearing several groups of Teddy Boys away from shop doorways with the now familiar flick of the gloves the constable asked Graas if he wanted a ball bearing. 'I only have one to spare,' he said. 'It's better than nothing.'

'No, it's alright,' replied Graas. 'But do you fancy going down to Newbridge Road bakery tonight?'

'No, not tonight, Roland,' replied the constable. 'We have new management – a sergeant – on the shift. Just been promoted to uniform from CID he has. Keen as hell he is too. The sort who would summons his own granny if he got the chance. No doubt he wants to get back to CID, so he will be on the lookout for anything that will bring him to the attention of the powers that be. Catching me off Holderness Road would be a real feather in his helmet, but he's got no chance. Joined the same day as me, he did. Clever pratt, he got his promotion exams before I could even sit them and I haven't got mine even yet. We didn't see eye to eye when we were in training and he knows that I think that he's a right pillock. He bought his own house a few months back. I've only got a new Council house on Longhill estate. He thinks he's a budding chief constable, he does. Puts on a posh accent too he does. His wife is a schoolteacher. She comes from Beverley but he was born down Lister Street. Tends to look down on me now, he does. I'm watching my back with him around. Bloody bakery cockroaches can have a free pardon and a lease of life for a while. Pity we don't have a cockroach or two on Holderness Road mind.'

'You wouldn't want him to know about cockroach killing then,' commented Graas.

'Wouldn't mind that except the pillock would have a go at prosecuting me under the Protection of Animals Act 1911,' he replied.

'But cockroaches are not animals, are they? They are vermin. It's as simple as that,' replied Graas confidently.

'A cockroach is a beetle and, of course, a beetle is an insect. And an insect is not an animal, you are right,' replied the constable. 'But no, I shall give them all a lease of life for a while. You won't have met this pillock of a sergeant yet?'

'No,' replied Graas. 'I hope to meet him, though. You see, one day I would like to go into the CID.'

'Well, that's as maybe, Roland, but you need to think hard about that. Anyhow, meantime don't be too trusting with our new sergeant. And another thing, never tell him what the lads call me. Never tell him that, he would make a mockery of it,' said the constable.

'I don't follow,' replied Graas. 'Do you mean a nickname or something?'

'You are still bloody naïve aren't you, Roland,' replied the constable. 'Yes, of course, I mean nickname. The lads call you Baby-face. Didn't you know?'

'Do you mean that's what the men on the shift call me?' asked Graas.

'Good God, Roland. You are a lesson in naivety in itself,' replied the constable.

'Yes, the men on the shift. It's all innocent fun. No harm meant.'

'But what do they call you?' asked Graas.

'Mine is a nickname well earned, Roland. They call me VD and I am proud of it. I get rid of more vermin in east Hull than all the bobbies in the city put together. I get more cockroaches than rats, mind. Yes, that's me. The *Vermin Destroyer*. Every time I drop my truncheon – bottom end first – out of this world goes a bloody cockroach. Knackers to my number, lad, you can call me VD.'

Graas could hardly contain himself. 'You. VD. *Vermin Destroyer*. What a laugh,' chuckled Graas. 'I can't believe it. It's really funny.'

'I don't see it as so funny, Roland. It's only a nickname,' mumbled the constable. 'You have got an odd sense of humour, you have.'

Graas decided there and then that he would not mention anything about Inspector McWhoo's concern but now he knew he could tell the inspector what he had found out without really telling any tale that might cause trouble or embarrassment to anyone – and hopefully it would help to secure the completion of his probationary constableship!

The following day he telephoned the Inspector at Crowle Street. Initially he told him that he had an answer to his query, but, before he could say anything further, the Inspector interrupted, saying, 'You have done very well, 129. I knew you would do it. I know a good nosey young policeman when I see one. No, don't say another word. Not a single word,' he added excitedly. 'Where are you calling from? I shall ride out to see you. This is to be classed as highly confidential.'

'I am at the Stoneferry section box sir, but . . .' replied Graas.

'Not a word, 129,' the Inspector interrupted. I shall cycle over to the Chapman Street telephone box. You meet me there. We must keep this quiet. Don't trust telephones. The PBX operator here pokes his nose into almost every call that comes in. I am on my way.' He hung up abruptly.

Graas left the Stoneferry section box and began his walk along

Stoneferry Road to Chapman Street, concerned that McWhoo was apparently so excited – and, knowing the reality of the situation, he was full of trepidation as he took the twenty minutes walk to meet him. However, he arrived in Chapman Street and was beside the telephone box near the River Hull bridge several minutes before the Inspector. Looking along Chapman Street towards Dansom Lane, he eventually saw McWhoo coming towards him peddling quite fast, as if peddling with all his might. Pulling up alongside him, McWhoo took his uniform cap off, wiped his brow and said breathlessly, 'I am sorry I am a bit late, 129. I was delayed at Crowle Street. No matter though. I knew you were the right man to delve into such a sensitive issue. Who is it?'

'Well, sir. I hope you will not be disappointed but I . . .'

Interrupting once more, McWhoo said impatiently, 'Don't dilly dally, lad. The constable's number is all I want. Who is it?'

'If you will let me finish, sir. I will tell you,' said Graas as McWhoo replaced his cap. 'There is no one on the shift with VD – at least I don't think so.'

'What? I have just ridden over here from Crowle Street because you said you had the answer I wanted,' uttered McWhoo, who was now clearly annoyed. 'Don't you dare flannel me, 129. What are you playing at? You can't possibly know that no one has VD. Now you are annoying me.'

'I told you I have an answer sir, and I have. But you have been barking up the wrong tree when you were thinking that VD means venereal disease,' said Graas.

'In my book it's the only meaning it can have. Don't mess with me, 129. I'm old enough to be your father. It's VD and nothing but VD, so don't come up with excuses. I want to know who it is and I want to know now,' demanded McWhoo.

With an uncontrollable chuckle Graas then said, 'In this case it means *Vermin Destroyer*, sir.'

There was a brief pause and a touch of momentary embarrassment; then McWhoo spluttered, '*Vermin Destroyer, Vermin Destroyer.* What on earth are you talking about?'

'I can't really tell you, sir, but one constable in this division has the habit of bashing cockroaches into the ground with his truncheon so the lads recently nicknamed him VD. That's all there is to it, sir, honest,' said Graas as he began to chuckle again.

'You will laugh at the other side of your face in a minute, 129,' said McWhoo threateningly. 'Woe betide you if you are making this up. Indeed, giving a superior officer a load of bunkum is a discipline offence. I shall only be satisfied if you give me the man's name. Now then, who is it?'

'Just can't tell you, sir. I am not a person who tells tales, but I am telling you the truth. It would not be fair to give you the name. You wouldn't give the name if you were in my shoes, would you, sir?' Then with a tongue in cheek approach he continued, 'When all is said and done you are the one to be admired, sir. Admired because of your principles and all round reputation. Actually I am doing my best to model myself on your qualities, that's all, sir.' The Inspector began to finger and straighten his tie, and, appearing embarrassed, he said, 'Well, I take that as a nice compliment, 129.' He gazed down at the kerb for several seconds and then said, 'Alright. I believe you. I was wrong, but I did think it meant VD. I am sure you would if you were in my position.'

Only too happy to agree with his inspector, Graas replied, 'Indeed I would, sir. I am pleased and in fact reassured knowing that I have an inspector of your calibre to speak to in my early service in the force. Keeping confidences is what it is all about, isn't it, sir?'

Inspector McWhoo mounted his bicycle and saluted Graas before Graas had the chance to salute him first. 'You are doing very well, 129. Your kind words are greatly appreciated. Not many constables are willing or indeed have the notion to express their admiration like you have done. Thank you.'

He then rode off towards North Bridge. A few moments later he came cycling back again. 'Cockroaches, 129. Where does he find the cockroaches?'

'Oh, apparently he finds them on the ground, sir. They don't often fly you know.'

'I see,' muttered McWhoo thoughtfully. 'Of course they don't fly – not cockroaches. 'He then rode off again seemingly pre-occupied with his thoughts.

Graas was relieved to see him go again and even more pleased to feel that the pressure on him to reveal the Inspector's suspect VD carrier was gone for good.

Later the same day Inspector McWhoo approached Graas as he was patrolling Lime Street beside the River Hull. 'I trust that you will not say a word about me thinking that we had got someone in the division suffering from VD?' he said. 'I would look a real fool if the men knew that. They are not all so understanding as you, 129.'

Graas could not help but smile broadly as he replied, 'Oh, you do flatter me, sir. Of course, I shall keep it, as you said on the phone earlier, "highly confidential", sir. We must help each other in this job, mustn't we, sir.'

'You have a self-satisfied smile on your face. What are you thinking about, 129?' asked McWhoo.

'Oh, I was just thinking that I am happy to keep the confidence, sir. That's all. It's a happy smile, not a self-satisfied smile,' he replied.

'That's fine then, 129. I have a copy of the memo the Chief Constable issued some time ago about management.' Reaching into his jacket pocket, he continued, 'Here take this carbon copy. Keep it to yourself. I am sure that you will reach senior rank in the years to come, then maybe it will be worth your while reflecting on this paper and the management skills you have noticed I have. I told you a while ago I would give you a copy.'

He handed four sheets of foolscap size paper to Graas saying, 'Keep it to yourself now. Don't forget; keep quiet about the VD thing. Even I, a police inspector, can be wrong just occasionally.'

'Yes, sir,' replied Graas.

'By the way,' commented McWhoo. 'I bought a Morris Minor Traveller car recently, you know. Cost £570. That's the best part of a year's pay to you. I'm getting on a bit now and don't want to be riding a bicycle forever. Wife and me will now be able to go to places like Bridlington, Scarborough and Withernsea in the car instead of the train. If you keep working conscientiously, maybe in ten years or so you will be able to buy a little Morris Minor too.'

He then rode away, obviously feeling perfectly happy with his little world.

Shortly afterwards Graas had the chance to look at the papers the inspector had given him. Sure enough it was a memorandum from the Chief Constable to his senior officers. It stressed the need for the strict observance of the Chief Constable's orders. In the paper the Chief stated that he regretted to have to state that he had noticed a tendency for senior officers to offer excuses for men who had been guilty of neglect of duty or failure to comply with instructions. It was also pointed out that senior officers who failed to take appropriate and strict action against defaulters were also neglecting their own duty, adding that, unless there is punishment for indiscipline and neglect, there is obviously no recognition for good service. The memo, consisting of some twenty carefully and stringently worded paragraphs, was obviously circulated by Sidney Lawrence to show that he knew what police discipline was about and that he intended to enforce it, no matter who the defaulter was. Behind it all was Sidney's ambition for the people of Hull to have good, sound and efficient policing. His efforts were to be rewarded. Within a few years Hull City Police Force was to become one of the finest constabularies in the country.

Gripe Water

Crime detection had a perpetual fascination for Pc Graas. The very reason he become a policeman was that he believed he had the kind of inquisitive mind that would do well in the investigation of criminal activity. He had made several arrests for breach of the peace, drunkenness and even wilful damage but he had not yet arrested anyone for real crime. And, regardless of Sergeant Doyle's earlier comments about pansies in window boxes, he had not found anyone to summons for such things. It was hard to find dandelions in Nornabell Street, let alone pansies.

Despite his early thoughts of maybe being allowed to go straight into the CID without first carrying out uniform duties, he now knew that he had to complete two years walking beats before he had any hope of becoming a detective. And no one in the division appeared to give him any encouragement to become a detective either. It was almost as if every uniform man was resentful of their trilby hat colleagues. An added difficulty was that he was being given no chance to show that perhaps he could detect crime. 'That's for the CID, 129. Leave it to them. We can take the complaints of crime and record it, but the rest is up to the detectives, not you,' was Sergeant Clive Nile's comment one day. 'And any hurry-up calls are for the traffic department car patrols to attend, not you. Walking your beat is preventing crime, that's all there is to it. A policeman walking about the streets frightens would-be criminals off,' old Sergeant Nile added.

There was only one thing to do, thought Graas one day. I shall keep my eyes peeled and try my luck at catching a thief myself. There must be someone I can catch who is stealing something somewhere. Prevention of crime by examining shop doors and windows every night and weekends is one thing. He had had plenty of that but crime detection was going to be his main objective from now on, no matter what Sergeant C. Nile might think.

Patrolling along the terraces of Kent Street one sunny afternoon Graas spotted a young man who came hurrying into the Street from the direction of Dansom Lane. He was pushing a quite new-looking Silver Cross pram. As he hurried by, Graas glanced into the perambulator and saw that, whilst it had a quilt and pillow under the upturned hood and a cover over the bottom end, it did not contain a baby.

'Just a minute. I want a word with you,' he called out. The young man stopped, hesitated, and then said, 'I have only been to the chemist in town. Baby has been a bit sick. Wife is looking after baby so I went and got some groceries as well. I only live up top of the street.'

'There are chemists on Holderness Road. Why go into the city centre?' asked Graas.

Lifting up the pillow, Graas saw a length of rolled-up curtaining and beneath that several tins of foodstuff. Holding on to the pram handle the young man said, 'Curtain comes from Zimmerman's new cash furnishing stores in Paragon Street. See, price label is still on. Groceries, well they come from different shops. Nowt is nicked if that's what you are thinking, officer. Can I go now? See, baby needs the medicine, that's why I have been hurrying.'

'What's wrong with the baby?' asked Graas.

'Stomach. Yes, he's got stomach pains. I reckon it's just wind. Missus drinks a drop of beer, you know,' he replied.

'Then you will have some gripe water, won't you?' asked Graas.

With a faint smile the young man replied, 'You should have been a doctor, officer. That's right. Gripe water. I have just got some. I'd best be off and give it some,' he said.

'Can I see it before you go. There is good gripe water and some that's not so good. What sort have you got?' asked Graas.

'Oh, it's in there somewhere. I just asked chemist for gripe water, that's all. I don't know so much about these things as you do, officer,' he replied patronisingly.

'Then let me see it, please' asked Graas.

The man began rummaging through the pram under the pillow but Graas noticed that he did not bother to remove the cover at the lower end of the pram. With a gut feeling that something was amiss, but wanting to ascertain the man's address, Graas wanted to avoid giving the impression that he was satisfied that all was well. So he joined the man in idle chatter as they walked along Kent Street and to the end of a terrace at the Holderness Road end of the street. At the door of the little two-up-and-two-down terrace house, Graas helped the man lift the pram over the doorstep and into the narrow passage inside. Significantly he noticed that there were no scrape marks from the pram on the passage wallpaper or the door frame. With so narrow an entrance the pram would surely have banged against the wall when, one would think, the mother would normally struggle to get the pram through the door, over the step and in and out of the passage. Graas also saw that there was no lampshade over the electric light in the passage. Possession of a new-looking Silver Cross pram but no lampshades did not add up. Once inside, Graas asked, 'Now then, let's see the gripe water!'

At that moment a young woman carrying a baby little more than a few weeks old came into the passage from the back room. 'Gripe water? We don't have any gripe water. Baby's on breast-feeding. We don't need gripe water.' She continued, 'A bobby coming in here wanting gripe water. Whatever next! She then stopped abruptly, stared at the pram now parked in the passage between Graas and the young man. 'Don't tell me you've been getting more stuff on HP, Leonard,' she said. 'And what's this bobby doing here wanting gripe water? Beer and cups of tea is more in his line, isn't it? Gripe water is for babies, not a young bobby.

You will have the whole of Kent Street talking about us with him here. Neighbours will never believe a bobby just walked in here for a drink of gripe water.'

Standing beside the pram Graas gently lifted the cover at the bottom end. 'What have we got here then?' he enquired as he picked up two well-worn purses that were partly stuffed down the side of the pram alongside two pairs of yellow ankle socks.

'How did they get there?' asked Leonard.

Graas opened the first purse and counted out two one-pound notes, a ten-shilling note, two florins, a sixpenny piece and two halfpennies. Making a total of £2. 14s. 7d. In the second purse he counted out four one-pound notes, four half-crowns, five shilling-pieces and two three-penny bits, making a total of £4. 15. 6d. There was also a prescription form from Doctor Percy Scott of Beverley Road to a Mrs. Ellis.

No one spoke a word as Graas quickly counted the money. The young woman continued to cuddle the baby and Leonard simply looked up at the ceiling. As Graas made a scribbled note of the amounts he had counted, the woman said, 'What did you bring him home for, you damned fool. You should have told him to go to the chemist's for his gripe water. Now, look what you have done. Couldn't you see he's a young bobby looking for promotion?'

'Oh, I didn't bring him here, he just came with me like a bloomin' stray dog. Followed me here he did,' replied Leonard.

'Come on, Leonard,' interrupted Graas. I want to know where you got these things? Do you want to tell me?'

'Course I don't want to tell you. What a stupid question, but I've no choice, have I? Look, you might as well know. I've pinched the lot. Food, all of it. Purses come from women's shopping bags as they walked along Jameson Street. Nobody suspects you when you're pushing a pram. Only old women ever want to look in pram and I'm too quick for them.'

The hair on the back of Graas's neck began to bristle with excitement as he realised that there, right in front of him, he had discovered for the very first time a real thief. A real criminal, no less. He placed his hand on the truncheon hanging down inside his trousers beside his right leg, ready to pull it out should there be any violence, but realised instinctively that Leonard could easily be handled by words more than action. He released the grip on the truncheon.

Gathering his thoughts, Graas said, 'What do you mean when you say "the lot"?'

'Everything. The pram as well,' replied Leonard. 'All the tins and packets of food. The curtain material, the socks. All of it. It's all nicked. I got it all in City centre this morning. Purses; well, I didn't know how much was in them, but they were easy. Women going around with purses on top of their shopping bags are easy. It's just likely they think they have lost them, not stolen. The pram was easy too. Left outside

Zimmerman's. I watched the owner go inside with her baby. I just wheeled it away. No baby in, mind. Who would nick a baby? That would be daft. But, come on, what did you have to speak about bloody gripe water for? If you hadn't spoke about gripe water I wouldn't have told you I'd got some when I didn't. Why don't you just walk your flaming beat looking important and minding your own business? Nobody else bothered me not having baby in pram. Even the bobby on traffic duty on North Bridge didn't stop me. Good bloody bobby him. He stopped traffic coming out of Lime Street to let me cross the road, he did.'

Graas interrupted Leonard's chatter by uttering the official caution, 'You are not obliged to say anything unless you wish to do so and whatever you do say will be taken down in writing and may be given in evidence.'

'Go on, then, you had better take me to Crowle Street,' Leonard replied.

'I don't believe this,' exclaimed the now highly agitated young woman. 'You really are a silly man, Leonard. Pinching stuff's not so bad, but bringing a young bobby home with you with a nicked pram full of gear is ridiculous. What will the neighbours think? You might as well tell him you have done the gas meter as well. I aren't taking the can for that. What would my probation officer have to say?'

Graas took a quick look in the back kitchen and, sure enough, the prepayment gas meter cash container had been broken open. The lock lay on the floor and a shilling coin lay beside it. 'Spent it at Nag's Head the other night, he did,' said the woman.

'Yes, but I only got a couple of quid,' Leonard said.

Graas quickly assessed the situation. He was now already late for making the routine call to Crowle Street that he should have made from the Chapman Street telephone box. He now had a prisoner and a stolen pram partly full of stolen property to take care of – and there were no telephones in the street.

'You can leave the pram and the stuff here if you like,' volunteered the woman. 'I'll just let baby have a little sleep in it, then you can come back for it with a van later. It looks like the sort of pram they use in Kirkella or Beverley, don't it? You shouldn't have nicked such a good pram, Leonard. An old one would have been OK. I wouldn't dare use this around here anyway. Neighbours would know it was nicked.'

'No, I must take Leonard and all the stolen property to Crowle Street. Thanks all the same,' replied Graas.

He then told Graas formally that he was under arrest and then added, 'I would hate to think you would be the first person to be walloped with my truncheon if you do try to escape, Len.'

'Alright, alright, I know the routine,' he said. 'Some of your people know me at Crowle Street. One of your sergeants – the one with a load of hair growing on his nose – once nicked my Dad for pinching lead off a church roof.'

Leonard willingly helped Graas to get the pram and the contents out of the passage and into the terrace. Graas now had his very first criminal under arrest and had recovered the stolen property too. He felt good about it but it crossed his mind that Leonard might panic and make a run for it and escape. He knew also that to allow a criminal to escape was a disciplinary offence! He had carried a pair of handcuffs in his uniform trousers every time he was on duty but had never used them, not even for the few drunks he had arrested. However, no one actually told him when, or how, to use them, not even at the police training school. But now, he had something of a predicament on his hands. Leonard might escape and that would mean big trouble. The pram and contents was evidence of crime and he had a strict duty to care for it all. He was particularly concerned about the two purses which no doubt belonged to women who could ill afford to lose them. Graas also reasoned that if Leonard escaped as they were making their way to Crowle Street he would have to chase after him, leaving the pram and contents in the street. That being so, he reasoned, it would not be long before someone made off the lot.

'I don't want to embarrass you, Leonard, so I will tell you what I am going to do,' he said. 'You are under arrest. You already know that. Well, if you escape you will be charged with escaping from police custody and I will be charged before my chief constable with letting you escape. Now we don't want that to happen, do we? I don't want to embarrass myself either and I will if I push this pram along the street and all the way to Crowle Street, me being in uniform with a helmet on. So I'm going to handcuff you to the pram handle. With your jacket on, the jacket sleeve will hopefully cover up most of the handcuff on your wrist. You can walk to Crowle Street and I will walk a few yards behind you. That way I am sure that all will be well. If you try to do a runner you will not get far handcuffed to the pram. Anyway, this way will save you the temptation of escaping. By the way, just as a reminder, I have not yet christened my truncheon!'

'Hurry up and get them on before any of the neighbours see,' he replied as the young woman stood in the passage before slamming the door shut behind them.

Graas quickly applied the handcuffs to the pram handle and then to Leonard's left wrist and told Leonard to walk at a normal pace to Crowle Street. They were soon walking along Holderness Road, over the Southcoates railway crossing next to Waller Street, and, as they passed the Nag's Head on the Waller Street corner, a middle-aged woman called out to Leonard, 'Got your bairn a nice pram then, Lenny.' Leonard ignored her and kept walking. She saw Pc Graas glance towards her as he followed Leonard. 'Miserable man. I was only asking him about the bairn.'

'Never mind, missus,' replied Graas with a knowing smile. 'Maybe he's got something on his mind just now.'

They continued along Holderness Road before turning into Craven Street, with Graas keeping a good fifteen yards behind his manacled pram thief. As he guessed, no one appeared to notice that Leonard and the pram were actually locked together. As they made their way along Craven Street and up the slope of the Craven Street bridge near Hedon Road, Graas heard the sound of Sergeant Nile's voice coming from behind. 'Where do you think you are going, 129?'

Graas then saw the wiry, unpopular and self-important Nile pulling up on his bicycle on the opposite side of the road as he shouted out across the hum of the traffic, 'Hey, 129! You didn't make your routine call from Chapman Street. I was waiting for you there. Now I have caught you away from your beat. What do you think you are doing?'

Graas kept walking, not wishing to lose sight of Leonard and the stolen goods. 'I am going to Crowle Street, sergeant,' he shouted back.

A few moments later Sergeant Nile ran up and alongside Graas, pushing his bicycle with one foot on a pedal like a child with a toy scooter. With his voice raised he said, 'Going to Crowle Street? You had better get back to your beat, 129. You don't have permission to go to Crowle Street, let alone leave your beat. And stand still when I'm talking to you.'

'I can't, sergeant,' replied Graas, as Nile became increasingly annoyed.

'If you want to relieve yourself you can go behind a wall or something. You don't need to go to Crowle Street just to relieve yourself,' Nile answered.

'Good heavens, sergeant,' Graas replied. 'I don't want to relieve myself. Whatever gave you that idea?'

'My experience of life tells me that someone who can't stand still usually wants to go to the toilet. If you don't want to go then stand still, that's an order!'

With an expression of annoyance on his face and raising his voice, Graas said, 'Sergeant, I have arrested that man up ahead. See, the man pushing the pram over the bridge towards Hedon Road.'

'What? What? Arrest did you say?' replied Nile. 'Don't tell me lies, 129. If you have arrested him you would be holding him by the arm in the approved manner, or have him handcuffed.'

As Sergeant Nile scooted his bicycle gently alongside, Graas saw that Leonard was gradually increasing the distance between them so he turned to Nile and said, 'You are slowing me down talking as you have, sergeant. Why don't you go to Crowle Street. I will see you there in a few minutes.'

'Are you alright, 129? asked Nile. 'Haven't lost your marbles, have you? Stand still I order you.'

Continuing to follow Leonard and the pram, Graas replied, 'Look, man. I have arrested that man pushing the pram. The pram was stolen in the City centre this morning and I am taking him to Crowle Street. If he gets away it will be because you have interfered with what I am doing. He could just run along Hedon Road and be away. I am sorry but I'm going. I intend to keep up with him. You can scoot along with me if you like; otherwise shut up until we are at Crowle Street.'

'How dare you speak to me like this? I shall report this right away. If that man is under arrest you are chancing your luck, 129, let alone the way you have spoken to me. And where are your handcuffs? If you thought that he was going to escape you should have used the handcuffs, that is what they are for!' said Nile.

Not wishing to exasperate the situation further, Graas ignored the remark and hurried on after Leonard, leaving the sergeant scribbling something in his notebook. No doubt number 129 figured prominently there.

Leonard was waiting at the Hedon Road junction just across from the Oriental public house where Graas reached him. 'What happened to you then?' he asked. 'I would have felt a right Charlie going into the cop shop handcuffed to this damned pram all by myself.'

'Never mind, Leonard. Let's go,' replied Graas with a smile.

After a short walk along Hedon Road past the Alexandra Dock entrance they arrived at Crowle Street police station. Graas noticed that Sergeant Nile was following them about fifty yards back and pushing his bicycle. Still handcuffed to the handle, Leonard could do little but help Graas lift the pram from the pavement to the front doorstep and into the police station, then along the highly polished passage and into the station sergeant's office. The office also doubled as a charge office with several cells behind it. Graas was now happy and just a little proud that he had got his first criminal to the station without too much of a problem. Suddenly a voice boomed out from along the corridor. 'What the devil do you think you are doing, 129? The bloody maternity hospital is further up the road. We don't allow prams in 'ere. Get it out.'

Graas immediately recognised the gruff voice of the Divisional Chief Inspector who came striding along the corridor towards him. He was red faced and obviously very angry. 'Just look at the dirty wheel marks on this floor. We pay cleaners to polish this floor and in case it has escaped your notice we don't want all the filth from Hedon Road littering our floor!' he thundered.

The Chief Inspector, who was nearing the end of his service, was known as an arrogant, humourless, self-important man who appeared to enjoy humiliating young constables. Perhaps because of this the atmosphere in Crowle Street in those days was not jolly, and all those working there were rather glum and lacking in any kind of the good-natured behaviour that was thought important to good policing. This day appeared no different.

'The pram is stolen, sir,' ventured Graas anxiously.

'Then take it out and bring it in through the back door, lad. We don't bring stolen goods in by the front door, do we?' growled the Chief Inspector.

'But I am practically in the charge office, sir. I have to bring stolen goods into the charge office,' replied Graas.

'I don't care where you have to bring stolen goods. You came in by the wrong door. Now get out and come back in via the back door. And take this pram pushing nitwit with you!' shouted the Chief Inspector.

'I go where the pram goes, mate,' said Leonard rather cheekily.

'Mate, mate. You call me a mate. I am not your bloody mate,' the Chief Inspector said. 'I'll have you locked up if we get any more lip from you. If that pram is nicked you'd better get your hands off it. It doesn't belong to you, does it?'

'No,' replied Leonard.

'Then get your hands off,' said the Chief Inspector raising his voice in apparent rage. 'Your bloody fingerprints will be all over it!'

'I aren't got "bloody fingerprints", mate. I aren't a wife beater,' replied Leonard. 'Anyway, this young bobby has got me hooked to it with his handcuffs. I can't let go until he unlocks me. He's got me tied to it like a dog to a kennel. Look!'

The Chief Inspector glared at the pram handle and handcuffed wrist in amazement, then said, 'Good Lord above! I thought I'd seen it all, but this is preposterous. We don't 'cuff members of the public to prams, 129. You'd better get this contraption and the attached person out of here and back again by the recognised door, the back door before I get really upset.'

'But taking it and him along the passage and out through the front door and in again through the back door and along the passage again seems stupid to me, sir, 'answered Graas. He hesitated for a moment then expressed what he was thinking, saying, 'This man is a prisoner. I've arrested him and – I hope you don't mind me saying this, sir – but you shouldn't try to humiliate me in front of a member of the public, and a man under arrest at that. It stinks of poor management.'

'Do it,' bellowed the Chief Inspector. 'And remember you are only a probationer.'

Being annoyed by the veiled threat but also feeling apprehensive about the ineptitude of his so-called superior officer, Graas said, 'I shall do it, sir, but I do think that you should remember that whatever is said in the presence of a prisoner will be recorded in my official notebook. That is the law.'

The Chief Inspector's face became deep red again and looked as if it was about to explode. He directed a ferocious scowl at Graas, pointed to the front door, and in a loud voice said, 'Get out! Get out! Don't you quote the law at me! I learned about the law before your mother took the risk of letting you crawl about the kitchen floor without nappies!'

Sensing that he had over-stepped the mark with his comments, Graas and the tethered Leonard quickly lifted the pram up and carried it out into the street through the front door. Where was Sergeant Nile? He had been following them from Craven Street and he was not far behind them when they entered the front door. Now there was no sign of him. However, as they walked around to the back of the police station they saw Sergeant Nile standing in the backyard leaning against his bicycle. 'I saw you going in the front door, 129,' he said with a flicker of a smile. 'If I had come after you it would look as if I had told you to go in that way. It's all right at night but the Chief Inspector has a thing about constables using that entrance in the daytime. I guessed you knew. I bet he sent you around the back here.'

'You must know that he did, sergeant. Your advice is too late,' replied Graas as he and Leonard trundled the pram and contents through the back door. They went along the passage and into the charge office where the station sergeant was sitting at his desk. As soon as they were inside Graas removed the handcuffs from the pram and the prisoner, then searched him and told the sergeant how he had found Leonard in possession of the pram and other things he believed were all stolen. The sergeant accepted Graas's account and wrote Leonard's details down on a detection form. As he wrote Leonard said, 'That's a nice Parker pen, sergeant. I have got two like that in the pram. Got them from Woolworth's, King Edward Street, this morning. Nicked a bottle of ink as well. It's all in the pram.'

Graas then took Leonard into a nearby cell, where he was detained. As Graas was about to lock the cell door Leonard said quietly, 'Fancy working for a pratt like that Chief Inspector. I didn't know your bosses were like that. Don't worry, though. I shall plead guilty to everything. Don't see any point in giving you more trouble. I'd tell them to stuff the job if I were you. By the way, you should have searched me when you arrested me, you know, but don't worry, I won't tell those pratt bosses about it.' A complete search of the pram shortly afterwards revealed, that, true to his word, Leonard did have two Parker fountain pens and a bottle of ink along with the other stolen goods.

Sergeant Nile was now standing in the doorway of the charge office. 'See what you have done, 129. I have got to get a constable to cover your beat as well as his own now that you are playing at being a detective. Don't you understand that a constable walking his beat prevents crime and that is what your job is, walking a beat?'

Graas, feeling more irritated by the minute, replied, 'And I suppose that you would say that I should ignore any possibility of detecting crime, sergeant. Come on. I thought you should be helping me, not grumbling at me all the time. I have recovered someone's pram, you know, and a lot of shoplifting stuff, and two purses with money in them.'

Nile made no comment. Graas then went into a nearby office, made his evidence notes in his notebook, and then telephoned the CID in Queens Gardens to enquire if the Silver Cross pram, the two purses and the other property had been stolen. He was told that the pram certainly had been reported stolen and that at least two purses had been reported stolen in the City centre earlier in the day. Just as he replaced the telephone handset, the Chief Inspector entered the room followed by Nile. 'You have shown considerable initiative with this arrest, 129,' he said with a smile. 'The station sergeant has told me about how you came by it and how you got the stolen goods and your prisoner down here to Crowle Street. Well done.'

'I was about to say the same thing, sir,' commented Sergeant Nile. 'Well done, 129. It's a pleasure having you on my shift.'

'Now, how are you getting on with your notebook entries, lad? asked the Chief Inspector. 'Remember, you should always make contemporaneous notes.'

'I have as far as possible, sir,' replied Graas. 'Actually I have just heard that the pram was in fact stolen from outside Zimmerman's Furnishers this morning.'

'That's good, 129. Now let me have a look at your notebook and then we shall leave you to get on with it,' said the Chief Inspector.

Graas handed his notebook over. The Chief Inspector looked at the latest entries carefully and then said, "Well, that's good, 129. Good that you haven't made a note about me rollicking you about coming in the front door. No good making notes of what I said in the presence of the prisoner, is there? I wouldn't want to be drawn into the court proceedings. After all, what I said was hardly relevant, was it? In any case I wouldn't want to be getting in on the act. My presence in court would take the shine off your efforts, you know. But don't you ever throw the law at me again. Do you hear? I am sure that you don't need reminding again that you are still a humble probationer and that I am the one who decides your future.'

Graas replied, 'I don't need reminding. I am reminded enough as it is. I must say, though, that I can better understand now how the police force loses men during their probationary time and why men don't join up as readily as they might. If I had my way I would certainly introduce some courses in good management and commonsense, but then I'm only a probationer.' He then left the room in silence, expecting a thunderous roar from the Chief Inspector, but there was none.

Leonard appeared before the Stipendiary Magistrate the following morning and was remanded on bail for a week. He then pleaded guilty to eight charges of theft. After the evidence had been heard, Graas was called to the witness box to give Leonard's antecedent history to the court. He added that he thought that Leonard would, in his opinion, make a good citizen provided he was given suitable professional advice and guidance from a probation officer. The Stipendiary, Mr. D. N. O'Sullivan, placed Leonard on probation for two years.

Shaking hands with Graas in the corridor soon afterwards and with a broad smile, Leonard said, 'I was expecting six months down the road. Thank you. Now we are both on probation, aren't we?'

Of course, Graas did not know it then, but in the years to come Leonard was to prove to be one of the best informants Graas could ever wish for.

Confidential Matters

Graas was now feeling happy and confident in his work. Happy that he had stood up to the Chief Inspector and fascinated by the way Inspector McWhoo now appeared to be his friend. He was also happy that he had actually arrested the pram thief, in fact his first real criminal arrest, and he was now confident that he would complete his two years' probation successfully. Indeed he was now well over half way through the two years' probation period, and the arrest of the pram pusher would no doubt have come to the notice of some of the city detectives.

Apart from that, he had attended several domestic disputes and given advice to several quarrelling couples – only one man had threatened to throw him out of the house. He had also attended nine road traffic accidents, one fatality on Preston Road, made several arrests for drunkenness, three for breach of the peace and four for wilful damage. He had also arrested two dock labourers for using obscene language outside the Astoria cinema on Holderness Road. The obscene language charges did become very embarrassing for young Graas, however. When the accused appeared in the Magistrates court he found that having to use the exact obscene words the dockers used in order to prove the case against them in court was very embarrassing. Having to use the exact words was bad enough in the atmosphere of the court, but, when one elderly woman magistrate asked him to explain the meaning of the offending 'f' and 'c' words, he became more abashed than ever as he did his best to explain and define the offending words. 'I shall turn a deaf ear to obscene words in future,' he muttered to himself as the case was found to be proven. He decided to let people swear if they wanted to and do no more than caution them, but even then only if he really had to. Swearing in the street was not so much a problem to him as it was having to repeat it all in the hushed dignity of a magistrates' court with the ever ready possibility of someone in the public gallery foolishly trying to smother silly pent-up giggles.

On point duty at the Holderness Road/Courtney Street junction during the five o'clock rush hour Graas saw two middle-aged detectives from Queens Gardens riding bicycles side by side along the road from the City centre. At that moment he was about to direct several cyclists and some cars coming from the direction of Reckitt's Dansom Lane factory, out of Courtney Street, and into Holderness Road so he stopped the two trilby-hatted detectives along with other traffic. 'Hello there!' he called and smiled as he acknowledged the two CID men now standing astride their bikes. Much to his surprise the two men looked down to their feet and ignored Graas completely. Graas noticed that one of them was much taller than the other. In fact the differences in their height made them look quite comical. Once the traffic flow from Courtney Street eased, Graas allowed the Holderness Road traffic to continue.

The two detectives pedalled on, continuing to ignore him. 'Miserable devils,' Graas murmured to himself. 'Anyone would think we were not in the same job.'

Half an hour later, after completing his traffic point duty, he went into the Holderness Road section box. There he found the same two detectives sitting in the small back office reading the *Hull Daily Mail*. Both were smoking Woodbines, and the little office reeked with an exhaust of tobacco smoke. 'What's your name, 129?' said one.

'It's Graas, Roland Graas,' he replied.

'Haven't you learned anything about this job, lad?' said the tall one as he took a great puff at his cigarette. 'You made a big mistake back there. You don't recognise detectives in public. Shouting out "Hello there!" is not on. What do you think we wear plain clothes for? It's so no one knows we're detectives.' The other detective butted in with a scowl on his face saying, 'Haven't you got any commonsense, lad?'

'Good grief, what a pair of miseries you are,' said Graas and then continued, 'Why, if you are wearing plain clothes, do you have to wear trilby hats? Two men in suits, wearing ties, and raincoats and riding bicycles side by side can only be detectives. No one else dresses like that. The hats are a dead give-away and well out of date for 1958. Everyone must know you are CID. I reckon you should give the public much more credit than you do.'

'What we dress in is our business but don't you ever make it obvious again that we are CID, that's all,' replied the tall one.

'I don't have to make it obvious. It already is, especially with those tatty, sweat-ridden trilby hats,' retorted Graas.

As the two detectives made to leave, the tall one said, 'You have a lot to learn, 129. We wear trilby hats because we have to. The Head of CID would not have it any other way. He believes that our hats give us an air of authority and dignity. When you have ten or more years in this job and you've made an arrest or two you might be in a position to criticise. Meantime, don't be so bloody sure of yourself. Nicking a chap pinching a pram and a couple of purses doesn't give you licence to shout your silly "Hello there!" across the street at us.'

Graas said nothing but followed them out of the section box and watched them push their bicycles along the pavement. In his view they looked far from dignified. Standing at the corner of Nornabell Street he watched them leave their bikes outside the Elephant and Castle and then go into the pub. It was just after opening time at six o'clock.

About half an hour later Graas was writing a road accident report in the section box when one of the detectives came rushing in. 'Someone has nicked my bike,' he shouted.

'Maybe the thief knew it was yours,' answered Graas. 'Why didn't you leave it here in the back yard? Never mind, I guess it's better pinching your bike than pinching that hat of yours.'

'You might not know it, 129, but I am a detective sergeant, so less of your impudence. You can get in my good books by keeping your eyes open for my bike. It is a green Hercules with a small puncture outfit bag fitted to the back of the saddle. It has two new Dunlop tyres, 28-inch wheels and Ever Ready lamps. I am not reporting it stolen officially. You wouldn't understand, but if I were to report it stolen from outside the pub, Detective Superintendent Cocksworth will see the report and then he'll know that I was in the pub at six o'clock.'

'Do you mean that you shouldn't have been in the pub?' asked Graas with an inquisitive smile.

'Look, you find the bike and let me know,' replied the Detective Sergeant. 'Meantime keep it all to yourself. I don't want any of your sergeants knowing about it either. One of them in particular would be in his glory if he knew my bike had been nicked.'

'Why?' asked Graas.

'He was kicked out of CID a couple of years ago when someone reported him for riding his bike apparently under the influence of drink,' replied the Detective Sergeant. He continued, 'He'd had a couple of drinks down, that's all. The powers that be couldn't prove anything, though. He was off duty and they couldn't find him at the time. The Chief Constable heard about it the next day and with no more ado posted him to uniform. He was a good thief catcher too and he's still bitter about the way he was dealt with. He'd report me just to get back in the good books of the bosses.'

'I shall keep my eyes open for your bicycle,' Graas replied. 'Where can I contact you should I find it?'

'Don't, whatever you do, leave a message at CID. Just bring it back to this section box. I shall check with you every day,' he answered.

'What if I find someone with it?'

'Don't arrest him. No don't even make a note of it,' replied the Detective Sergeant anxiously. 'Just take it off him. Tell him he's a lucky blighter. Tell him anything but don't nick him. Just get the bike. I can't stand the thought of being kicked out of CID and doing around-the-clock shifts in uniform for the rest of my service, and that is what would happen if it was known I was in the pub at this time. Officially we should have been keeping observations in Garden Village for someone who has been sneaking into houses and nicking stuff.'

The detective left in an apparent hurry, no doubt going off to keep observation in Garden Village – wearing the trilby hat.

'Is this all part of the force's strict discipline?' mused Graas. A detective has his bicycle stolen but does not report it for fear of being disciplined for being in a pub when he should have been elsewhere. Then to compound the situation he was telling young Graas to try to recover the bicycle but not arrest the thief or even make a note of the occurrence. It really was an insidious state of affairs and one that Graas was not willing to tolerate.

Fortunately Graas never saw any sign of the detective's cycle again and for several days afterwards he saw the detective peering out of the window of the Holderness Road trolley buses as he made his way from his home in Kingsley Avenue to Queens Gardens. Eventually the detective bought an old BSA bike from a Beverley Road second-hand bicycle dealer. Nothing more was said about the missing Hercules.

Late one evening, about ten days after the bicycle had been stolen, Graas spotted a similar bicycle leaning against a terrace wall in Endymion Street. It did not have new tyres as had been described by the detective on his machine, though. It was dark, but by the nearby street lamps Graas could see the bicycle quite well. He stood in the shadows for several minutes thinking that, regardless of the detective's instructions, he at least wanted to know who was stealing bikes on his beat.

Suddenly there was the sound of a loud metallic clatter coming from the end of a narrow passage behind some terrace houses in nearby Buckingham Street. Graas was by now well used to the sound of dustbin lids being upturned at night by marauding cats, but this was more than just a dustbin lid. It sounded as if a whole dustbin had been knocked over. With no more thought about watching for the possible bicycle thief, Graas grabbed the bicycle and dashed away with it and around to the passage from where he had heard the clatter.

It was quite dark in there but on shining his torch he was astonished to see a sergeant in uniform – the one who had very recently been promoted from detective constable to uniform sergeant – lying on the ground, face down beside an upturned dustbin with rubbish and coal ashes all around. A police helmet lay against a wall a few feet away. Without looking up, the sergeant, who was apparently in pain, said, 'My ankle, my ankle! I think it's broken.'

'Don't worry, sarge. Now is my chance to try out my first aid!' said Graas with obvious enthusiasm.

'First aid. First aid,' moaned the sergeant, but as he looked up he saw Graas and said, 'I don't want your First aid. What are you doing here?'

'I heard the dustbin fall and came to see what had happened, sarge,' replied Graas.

'Don't call me, sarge,' he hissed. 'It's a sign of unhealthy familiarity.' Then, glancing about the passage, he said, 'What's my bike doing here?'

'Oh, I brought it here,' replied Graas. Not wishing to reveal the secret of the detective's stolen bike, he quickly realised that the bike belonged to the sergeant on the ground. 'I thought some devil might pinch it, sergeant, and, thinking that you were busy down here I just made sure that it wasn't going to be stolen.' Then he added sarcastically, 'At training school I was told that part of my duty was to protect life and property. I have protected your bike. Now it appears I'm about to protect your life too.'

'Well help me up, man. Then wipe all this muck off me – and watch my ankle,' demanded the fallen sergeant.

'Yes, sergeant,' said Graas as he leaned over him. 'You have got yourself in a pretty mess, haven't you? What were you doing?' Graas brushed off some ashes and a piece of bacon rind from the sergeant's shoulders, saying, 'Shall I go and telephone for an ambulance? I had better not move you in case you've broken a bone or two. There is a phone box at the corner of Endymion Street.'

Looking dejected but at the same time trying to air his authority, the sergeant said, 'Never mind what I was doing; it's not your business. And no, I don't want an ambulance. Just get me up.' Graas then held the sergeant's outstretched right hand and was about to pull him up when the backyard door near the dustbin opened. Graas glanced into the doorway and saw a burly young man standing there with a partly dressed young woman close behind him. Graas automatically let go of the sergeant's hand. 'What's going on?' demanded the man menacingly. At the same time the young woman exclaimed, 'It's you, Walter. What have you been up to down there? Look at the mess you are in.'

'Walter? Who is bloody Walter?' asked the young man angrily.

'It's him, him down there, the sergeant. He was courting me a few years back. It is you, isn't it, Walter?' she said.

'So what's he doing here then?' asked the young man.

'Yes, what are you doing here, Walter, and with this young bobby. He was holding your hand, he was. What are you two doing down our passage?' she asked. Getting more excited and raising her voice she continued, 'Did you knock our dustbin over, Walter? If you did you'd better clear up all the mess. Look at it.'

The sergeant looked nervous and agitated. In fact Graas thought he was frightened too. 'Look, he's hurt his ankle,' Graas interrupted.

'Shut up, you!' shouted the young man. 'I'll give him bloody Walter. Pimping! Were you pimping us? I'll give you bloody pimping!' he shouted and glared down at the sergeant, at the same time giving him a hefty kick in the ribs. The sergeant groaned, cowered back and remained on the ground, looking helpless and stupid.

'This is assaulting the police on duty,' warned Graas.

'Duty! He might be on duty but he's not doing his duty. Can't be if he's bloody pimping,' said the young man as he continued, 'Coppers! Pimping coppers! What next? Where's his helmet? I'll bloody jump on it, then he'll have some questions to answer!'

Still subject to a certain amount of naïvety, Graas said, 'What is pimping, may I ask?'

'May I ask? May I ask? guffawed the young man. 'Can tell you are not from Hull, not with that fancy talk. Do you mean to tell me that you, a copper, don't know what pimping is?'

Graas replied, 'Well I know what a pimp is, but pimping must be Hull slang for something else. What does it mean?'

'Ask him down here,' replied the young man as he made something of a mock kicking action towards the sergeant who continued to languish on the ground.

Pulling him to his feet, Graas saw that although he had a bicycle clip on his left trouser leg just above his ankle, the right leg clip was missing and the trouser leg was held together with a piece of boot lace. There was a fair amount of grease on that trouser leg too that must have come from the sergeant's bicycle chain before he realised that the trouser clip was missing. As the sergeant got to his feet Graas saw he was now trembling and obviously no match for the young freebooter.

'I don't want any action taken against this man, 129,' muttered the sergeant.

'I heard that,' said the young man. 'He couldn't take action and he knows it. If you don't know what pimping is you have got it right here now. Your sergeant has been standing on our dustbin looking over the yard wall into our house trying to see us having a cuddle or something. That's pimping. The sneaky swine. No, he can't take any action as he calls it, 'cause if he did I would tell everybody what he was up to. Getting a good kick at him for free is justice enough for me. I should give him a good thrashing but look at him; he's a proper wimp. He doesn't look sensible enough to be a bobby, does he?

The sergeant began to hobble away along the passage, obviously in fear. 'Come on, 129, you come with me,' he said as he beckoned Graas to follow.

Graas turned but saw that the sergeant's helmet was still lying among the contents of the dustbin. He picked it up, brushed off some of the ashes and turned to follow the sergeant. 'You really didn't know what pimping was, did you? asked the young woman. 'Well it's bloody sneaking up on courting couples and watching what they are up to. It's kinky, sly and nasty if you ask me. That Walter is like that. I should know, and to think I could have married him.' Turning to her young man she said, 'Told you we should have closed the curtains, Charlie.'

'I'll kill him,' Charlie thundered.

He quickly calmed down, then turning to Graas said, 'Look, I'll give you a five bob for the helmet. I only want to smash it up, then I'll throw it into Barmston Drain on my way to Reckitt's in the morning.'

'No, I can't let you have it. Good grief. I would be in trouble for helping you to pinch it if I did, 'said Graas. 'And it's no good threatening to kill him either. He's not worth hanging for, is he?'

'No, but he makes me mad, he does,' he replied. Graas caught up with the sergeant, who was now leaning against his bicycle at the end of the passage. 'Not a word to anyone, 129,' he said. 'I've slipped on the kerb edge as I got off my bike and hurt my ankle, that's what happened. It's no concern of yours. In fact you must treat this matter as confidential. You didn't see anything. I am going to telephone Crowle Street from Endymion Street here and report sick. I shall make my own way home. I only live in James Reckitt Avenue.'

'Do you want your helmet, or shall I hand it in to Crowle Street for cleaning?' Graas asked sarcastically.

'Oh, God, no,' replied the sergeant as he reached out and grabbed the helmet. Graas was understandably annoyed about his behaviour and could not resist saying something to him. 'All right, sergeant, reporting sick is perhaps an easy way out for you.' Then Graas added quietly, politely and firmly, 'I think you should understand that I am far from happy with what I have seen, let alone what you have been doing here tonight. In fact, I am telling you now. Don't ever do anything like this again, especially on my beat. Furthermore, if I see or hear of anything like this again I shall have no hesitation in reporting you directly to the Divisional Superintendent. I don't care whether you are a sergeant or not. I take it that you only stooped to this sort of thing through some perverted ideas you appear to have about your former girl friend.'

73

The sergeant smiled weakly but let Graas's comments pass without riposte and limped off, pushing his bicycle alongside him without saying a word.

Graas already knew about confidential matters, what with the Inspector's VD error, the detective sergeant's unofficially stolen bicycle and now the uniformed sergeant's pimping escapade. 'Who knows,' he reasoned, 'keeping all these confidences would stand him in good stead for a chance to become a member of Special Branch where they kept confidences about such matters as Russian spy activity.' Actually he had once seen a Special Branch officer wearing a trilby and trying to hide behind a stack of timber at Drypool Dock, who, he guessed, was watching out for seamen from an East German ship. The secret work of the Hull Special Branch fascinated Graas but did not appeal to him as much as the work of the real detectives in the CID.

One thing was certain, though. If, and when, the opportunity came to join the CID, he would make it clear that he wouldn't, under any circumstances, wear a silly trilby hat!

A Touch of Vice

It is true to say that when Graas arrived in Hull he knew practically nothing about the ways of women of easy virtue, even though he had been in the RAF for five years. But, after being posted to east Hull and based at Crowle Street, it did not take him long to become familiar with their activities. Detailed to patrol and therefore keep order on that stretch of Hedon Road between Craven Street and Southcoates Lane, he was quickly educated by the night-time women with their tough looking pimps and clients at the 'all night cafés' opposite Alexandra Dock.

Enforcing the law on soliciting near the dock entrance was a regular feature at the 9.45 pm briefings of officers before they began their night duty. It is fair to say, however, that many constables did not consider soliciting a serious offence as no one ever complained about the 'girls'. Occasionally the arrest of a 'common prostitute loitering in the street for the purpose of prostitution' would be made on the instructions of the sergeant or inspector. Such arrests were most inconvenient for the constable, though, because of the practice in those days for the constable to go off duty at 2 am., then cycle home to get some sleep – hopefully he would get to bed by 3 am.– and then he would have to be up again just a few hours later to be well turned out and on duty at the Magistrates' Court in the Guildhall, by 9.45 am at the latest. The chances were that there would a long court list and a subsequent long wait in the court corridor before the case was called, sometimes after the lunch adjournment. Then, after giving his evidence and waiting for the conclusion of the case, he would cycle home and be ready for another tour of night duty at 9.45 pm In practice this would mean almost 24 hours without sleep. There was no such thing as overtime payments for constables. The fact that a constable was permitted to go off duty at 2 am instead of 6 am after making a soliciting, or for that matter a drunk person arrest, was considered compensation enough, one inspector claimed.

The commonsense view held by many enlightened constables was that heavy enforcement of the soliciting law simply caused the women to move elsewhere. As it was, there were few people actually residing beside the tumbledown Hedon Road cafés and no one living in the near vicinity ever appeared to complain. It was also believed that moving the prostitutes away from their Hedon Road patch would mean that the situation could not be easily contained, and the risk of frustrated foreign seamen perhaps seeking out some not-so-easy women in the City would be greater and much more troublesome.

In ordinary clothes Graas did not have the slightest appearance of being a policeman, perhaps that is why he was told to report on duty in plain clothes for several weeks. One such night he was instructed to accompany the one and only policewoman in the division to the Hedon Road area. His instructions were to report back to an inspector at Crowle Street all that he and his female plainclothes colleague observed, with particular reference to the prostitutes' pimps' vehicle registration numbers. One aspect he could not understand, however, was that there was no mention of prosecuting the local men who were often kerb crawling along that particular part of Hedon Road. In Graas's view, they were surely soliciting for sex just as much as the women. He was never afraid to speak up when given orders, but when he raised the kerb crawling aspect with its lack of emphasis on prosecution, the Inspector simply told him not to ask awkward questions. He let the matter rest there, for he was still subject to the two years' probation and testing of his conduct and character. Wanting to be fair to everyone, Graas decided that in order to frighten them away he would deal with any kerb crawler by questioning him and telling him – but without having any intention of doing so – that he would send a uniformed officer to his home within a few days to verify his address. However, most of the women's clients were foreign seamen who picked the women up at the cafés. Officers always left such seamen alone unless they were drunk and incapable or drunk and disorderly.

One way of discouraging the local kerb crawler was to follow the car with a client and picked-up prostitute to the quiet and poorly lit Corporation Road off Hedon Road and a few hundred yards up the road from the newly opened Oriental public house. The women appeared to prefer doing their actual business there probably because it was not far from the cafés, and they were not wasting precious time travelling from pick-up to purpose. Not having the luxury of a police car in those days, Graas and his colleague would walk the few hundred yards to Corporation Road, thus giving the client sufficient time to pay the fee to the woman before their business began. Then, timing it to perfection, Graas would dash up to the car, wrench a door open and announce that he was a police officer. Abuse would flow from inside and the kerb crawler would be short changed. The prostitute had done nothing to fulfil her obligations but would keep the money. The client's loss would be compounded by worry, waiting to see if a uniformed policeman would call at his home with some difficult questions. It was a Ways and Means Act preventative measure.

The Hedon Road prostitutes were – by and large – in the third, and often fourth, division of their profession. The smart, elegant and good-looking ones often ventured out to Leeds, Manchester and even London. Some of these could also be seen chatting up their clients in certain bars and hotel foyers in the centre of Hull, where they obtained rich pickings between their out-of-town trips. One of these was Barbara Snorthurst. One evening she was walking along Ferensway towards the Royal Station Hotel when a kerb crawler pulled up beside her and opened the near side window of his old Riley motorcar. At the same time, less than 50 yards away, Pc Graas was on duty in plain clothes. He was walking towards the Paragon Square police section box to make a telephone call and start a late evening tour of duty. Being alert, keen and thoroughly observant with a view to finding something to impress his superiors, he saw the Riley drive alongside Barbara. On the spur of the moment, and without giving it a great deal of thought, he decided to intercept the driver. A quick dash to the car was not quick enough, for, as he got beside the vehicle and was about to grab the nearside door handle, the driver accelerated away. Much to his amazement, Graas saw a barrister's wig box, gown bag and a brief case on the front passenger seat. Unfortunately he did not get a good look at the driver's face. He did, however, see that the driver was a male with greying hair. He also took note of the vehicle registration number. It had the familiar AAT number so he knew that it was registered in Hull at the George Street office. He would check it out when he had time, purely as a matter of interest.

'You have just lost me £20, you have,' snapped Barbara. 'Trouble with you is you aren't old enough to know much about my game. If you did you would leave a punter alone. And don't kid me, you young pillock. I know you are a damn copper. And don't think you can nick me soliciting either. I do my business from the hotel. I'm not one of them tramps from Hedon Road. I only have good professional clients.' She stormed off and made her way into the Royal Station Hotel. Graas thought better than mention what he had seen on the passenger seat of the car. But a kerb crawling barrister was quite a surprise.

Shortly after midnight a few days later Graas was again on plain clothes duty and waiting at a telephone box in Paragon Street when a well-dressed middle-aged man came up to him and said, 'Can I use the phone as soon as it is free? You see, I have been robbed.'

A robbery indeed! Graas could hardly contain himself. He had never ever dealt with a robbery. In his naïve excitement he could not resist getting involved and told the man that he was a police officer and on duty too.

'I must be getting old,' the man muttered. 'Are you sure you are the police? Well, you must be I suppose; only a fool would claim to be a policeman if he wasn't. You must understand this is a very embarrassing situation I'm in. Can we go somewhere out of sight and talk?'

Graas suggested that they go to the Paragon police section box. He agreed. Once inside, the man explained the events of the evening that culminated in him losing his wallet containing £150. He had visited the public bar at the Royal Station Hotel earlier in the evening. He was a local builder and had visited the bar, hoping to meet an old colleague. Whilst waiting he got into conversation with a tall, good looking, dark-haired and elegantly dressed 'businesswoman'. He bought her a drink or two and she took him to her flat near the Palace theatre on Anlaby Road. His former colleague did not turn up so he had time on his hands, he explained.

Whilst at the flat he realised, much to his horror, that the lady was a prostitute! Well, well, Graas thought, you never know, do you? Graas allowed the builder to continue his story, even though he did not accept everything said. The builder continued to relate his tale of woe, stating that he went to bed with the lady because it was late. The lady got up, saying she couldn't sleep, then took his jacket and trousers from a hook behind the door and asked him for payment for her services. He took the wallet from his jacket pocket and, as he did so, she grabbed the wallet, pushed him back on to the bed and ran from the flat. He quickly dressed, but by the time he got out to the street he could find no trace of her.

The poor – and foolish - man was in a dreadful state. He was a freemason, married with three teenage daughters and well-known in Hull and the East Riding society. An East Riding police inspector was one of his best friends, he said.

He wanted his wallet and money back. He would have willingly given her £5 but no more. 'Five pounds for less than five minutes' work is scandalous,' he said. He was annoyed by the 'impudence of the lady'. She had been charming earlier. 'How does a man know who's a prostitute and who isn't? he asked. Knowing that he could not always tell, Graas replied with a kind of childish boastfulness, 'You would easily know if you were in my business. We plain clothes men have a nose for this kind of thing.'

The builder made it plain that he wanted the prostitute found and prosecuted so Graas wrote down a statement of complaint detailing all that had occurred. The builder gave a good description of the woman too, but he did not know her name. Strictly according to the rules, Graas should have telephoned Central Division to report the crime and the matter would be passed on to the CID to investigate but he was so enthusiastic and keen to catch his first real robber that he decided to look into the crime himself.

The builder agreed to accompany Graas on foot along Anlaby Road to help identify the flat where the crime occurred. It was not long before he pointed to and identified a first-floor flat near the corner of Midland Street and Anlaby Road, and up the stairs they went. There was a light showing through a gap at the bottom of the flat door and Graas was quick to bang hard and loud on the grubby pink hardboard-panelled door. Amidst a fair amount of cursing from inside, the door was soon opened by a scraggy middle-aged woman who said, 'What the hell do you want? There is no need to bang the door down!'

Indicating the woman, the builder said, 'She wasn't here when I was here before. She's not the one who took my wallet.'

'No, I ain't taken no wallet. I'm respectable, I am. I do cleaning at Palace theatre, I do,' she said. 'What would I do with his bleeding wallet?'

'We're enquiring about the theft of a wallet,' announced Graas. 'Is there anyone else living here?'

'No, there ain't. If there were I wouldn't tell you two. It's none of your flaming business,' she replied. 'Get the cops if you want to but clear off. I'm going to bed.'

'I am a policeman, a City policeman in plain clothes,' Graas explained.

'Don't make me laugh!' she replied. 'Cadet maybe, but don't pretend to be a bobby when you ain't big enough. It will get you into trouble.' She slammed the door shut and Graas heard the sound of a metal bolt being shut inside. The builder shrugged his shoulders and followed Graas downstairs to the pavement.

'Are you sure you are a real bobby?' asked the builder as the pair began to walk along the street. 'Maybe you are just a cadet trying to impress your superiors. How am I supposed to believe that you are for real?'

Graas proudly showed him his Hull City Police warrant card that included his photograph, police number and Chief Constable Sidney Lawrence's signature. 'All right. I'm satisfied, lad. But I will be happier still when I get my wallet and 150 quid back. That would really impress your bosses,' he said with a smile.

Graas had learned that some City centre prostitutes used friends' houses for their business and felt that there was no chance of the woman being in the flat now. He accepted that she had long since disappeared with the wallet and the money. Anyhow, Graas was getting tired after keeping his eye open for pimps, their women and kerb crawlers all evening. All was not lost, however, because he knew that at CID HQ in Queens Gardens a very knowledgeable Detective Constable Dick Smith had a great reputation for identifying suspects by a modus operandi system on all sorts of criminals. Smith had built the system up over many years with male and female suspects. Graas decided to pay Dick a visit. In any case it would be an opportunity for him to visit CID HQ and maybe catch the eye of the proud and thoroughly conscientious Head of CID, Detective Superintendent James Cocksworth. Graas also reasoned that there was every reason to believe that no one would notice that he had not reported the wallet robbery to the CID in the first instance.

The builder agreed to meet Graas outside the Criterion cinema in George Street the following morning. From there they would go to CID by the back yard door. Constable Smith was located on the first floor in a room that had a huge table which held thousands of indexed cards with handwritten information about numerous criminals and suspects and all the methods they used in their criminal ways. Their addresses, pubs and clubs they used, their associates, aliases, tattoo marks, any deformities, scars, habits and so on were all recorded in an immaculate and easily retrievable card system that Dick had worked on conscientiously for ages. His was a craft to be admired. Of course, the police did not have the use of computers in the 1950s. It was over 25 years later that Hull police HQ received its first computer.

This was Graas's first case involving the modus operandi system. Knowing that Dick Smith was a man greatly appreciated by the Detective Superintendent, Graas made sure that he explained in detail all that related to the builder's misfortune the night before. As he gave the suspect's description and the address of the Anlaby Road flat, Dick announced, 'It's Barbara Snorthurst you want. She answers your description and, although I can't prove it, she's used a flat at the corner of Midland Street and Anlaby Road before. It is up on the first floor and just across the road from the 'dirty book shop'. Another woman lives there but she often visits friends in Park Street until the early hours and has an arrangement for Barbara to take her clients there. It's handy for the City centre you see and no doubt helps to pay the rent. Could be living on immoral earnings, I suppose.'

'But it can't be her,' said Graas. 'Snorthurst is blonde. I know her by sight. I saw her just a day or so ago near the Royal Station Hotel.'

Dick Smith chuckled as he said, 'You have a lot to learn, young man. She may have been blonde then, but I am telling you the woman you want is Barbara Snorthurst. And don't be surprised if she calls herself Veronica after the film star Veronica Lake when you find her. She has as many aliases as she has hair colouring. You will probably find her in a flat down Park Street. She usually stays in bed until mid-afternoon.'

Later that morning in company with a uniformed policewoman, Graas visited the flat mentioned by Dick Smith. It was just lunchtime. After several heavy knocks, and much to Graas's delight, Barbara answered the door. 'All right, you can come in,' she said. 'But why bring this old bag with you? Were you frightened I would lob you into bed or something?'

'No,' Graas replied. 'I'm not frightened. Why should I be?' The policewoman glared at Barbara but chose to say nothing.

'You would be, if you were alone, you young whippersnapper,' she said. 'I've eaten little boys like you for breakfast before today,' she replied with a laugh. 'What do you want, disturbing a girl from her slumbers at this time of day?'

Graas cautioned her and told her about the builder's allegation.

She sighed as if resigned to the obvious and said, 'You win some and you lose some. In my business you can usually count on clients keeping their mouths shut about any shenanigans for fear of being exposed, but somehow I had a feeling that this one would shout his mouth off. I should have known better.'

'Did you take the wallet?' asked Graas as he began to make notes in his notebook.

'Yes, I took his bleeding wallet. It's burned now and all the money has gone on clearing debt with rent and corner shop first thing this morning. Good job I did; otherwise you would have got it,' she replied.

'How much money was in the wallet?' asked Graas.

'£150. Mind you, he did have a good time and he was loaded. I thought he was one of them farmers from out Beverley way. He got his money's worth,' she said.

'But hardly £150 worth,' replied Graas.

'At your age that is something you would not know about,' she said knowingly. Glancing across the room to the policewoman she laughed out loud, saying, 'I must be getting bloody old. I've never seen such a young baby-faced bobby as this one before. Plain clothes one too.'

She began rumbling through her handbag, found a cigarette and lit it. Taking a large puff at it she went on, 'If this old bat were not with you I'd swear you were not for real – but wait a minute. You are the cheeky devil who frightened off one of my special clients outside the Royal Station the other day. I've got you now. A cheeky young bobby if ever there was one.'

'Never mind that now, Barbara,' said Graas. 'We now have to take you under arrest to the Central Police Station where you will be charged with robbery and, alternatively, the theft of the wallet and contents, the £150 that is.'

'Good job you've got her with you,' replied Barbara. 'Otherwise I could lead you a right merry dance.'

Dressed in smart maroon suit and looking very neat and tidy, Barbara appeared before the Stipendiary Magistrate, Mr. D. N. O'Sullivan, the following morning. She stood in the dock and pleaded guilty to the theft of the wallet containing £150. The more serious alternative charge of robbery was withdrawn. The prosecuting police inspector outlined the case and, standing in the witness box, Graas read out Barbara's antecedent history. On completion he told the Magistrate that he thought that with sound guidance Barbara had the makings of a good citizen. Before he had fully explained his reasons, Mr. O'Sullivan, who appeared slightly perturbed, interrupted saying, 'How can you stand here in my court and tell me that this woman, a known prostitute, would make a good citizen? Don't you fully understand her record?'

Feeling quite humble and very embarrassed, Graas said, 'It's just a thought, your worship.' The magistrate began writing something down in the court records on the desk in front of him. There was now complete silence in the courtroom. Graas remained in the witness box, too frightened to move. He stared at the Bible on the ledge at the front of the witness box but got little comfort from it. Glancing about the court he saw two known petty criminals standing in the public gallery. They were both smiling insanely, obviously getting much pleasure from seeing Graas being admonished by the Magistrate. The he inadvertently caught the eye of the prosecuting inspector who looked even more annoyed with him than the Magistrate.

The inspector beckoned Graas over to him. Graas walked quietly across to him but as he did so the Magistrate said, 'You have heard what this young officer has said about you. Goodness knows where he gets his idea of a good citizen! He obviously does not know you as well as this court. However, what have you to say about restitution? Can you repay the complainant?'

'I can if you give me a couple of hours,' she replied hopefully.

There was hushed laughter from the public gallery as Mr. O'Sullivan said, 'Then you will be allowed to go on bail until this court sits again at 2 pm this afternoon. That is two and a half hours away. Failure to be here then with the outstanding money will result in me sending you to Quarter Sessions for sentence. Do you understand?'

'I won't let you down, sir,' replied Barbara.

Mr. O'Sullivan then turned to Graas and said, 'Woe betide you if she fails to attend here at two o'clock sharp. One more thing: Don't ever play at being a magistrate or defence solicitor in my court again. I recall you coming up with this good citizen thing not so long ago. Don't ever do it again, in my court or any other court. I decide who is likely to be a good citizen and who is not, not you.'

'Yes, sir. Yes sir,' replied the highly embarrassed Graas. It did cross his mind to apologise but he decided against it as he felt that, the less

he prolonged the time standing there, the better. As it was, his heart was thumping so hard he was sure that the Magistrate could hear it pounding.

The Inspector told Graas that he would speak to him later – but never did.

Barbara hurried from the court and made off into Alfred Gelder Street and along the pavement towards Drypool Bridge. Good heavens, thought Graas as he began to follow her, dreading the thought that she would not keep the two o'clock appointment. Surely she was not going to throw herself into the River Hull? Not into all that slimy mud!

He hurried after her. Much to his amazement, when she got to the end of the Guildhall she dashed into the main entrance. By the time Graas got there she had disappeared inside. She could have walked through the Guildhall corridors without going out into Alfred Gelder Street, so why did she walk along the outside of the building and who was she going to see? Graas reasoned anxiously that maybe she didn't use the corridors because the Hull Quarter Sessions Court was sitting. He decided that she must be in the Guildhall somewhere and felt thankful that she was there somewhere, even though he didn't know where. Finding her in there somewhere would be much better than finding her in the muddy bottom of the river.

A long 30 minutes or more went by as Graas remained near the Guildhall eastern end-door. He had an ulterior motive in suggesting to Mr. O'Sullivan that Barbara would make a good citizen. It was little to do with whether he thought she would actually make a good citizen. He simply wanted to let Barbara believe that he had done her a favour by – hopefully – helping to avoid a prison sentence. Then, he gambled, she would be willing to help him with some information sometime in the future. But now, as time ticked away, he was getting more and more worried. Where was she?'

He was about to give up, feeling that she had given him the slip, when he saw her walking towards him from inside the Guildhall. She approached him, smiling broadly. 'I told you I would get it. But what's this about being a good citizen? I nearly laughed my head off when you told O'Sullivan that. Good job my mates weren't there. And you didn't please O'Sullivan either, did you? Anyway, I could not see any *Hull Daily Mail* reporters there so that's good. How could I live in my business if I was labelled in the paper as a good citizen.'

'No newspaper report will be a relief to the chap who lost his wallet mind,' Graas reminded her. Then he asked, 'How do I know that you have got the money – £150 – and where have you got it from? The Guildhall is not a bank.'

'Look, do me a favour. I've got the money. Maybe I know a barrister better than you do. Most of the girls pay their lawyers, don't they? Mine pays me. I suppose you would call it sort of payment in advance this time. I won't tell you his name, but he's a real sweetie. I've just seen him. A jury is out deliberating and that and he's got nothing to do but wait for the verdict. Good timing, isn't it? And you can tell O'Sullivan I ain't been on the game at lunch time – I've been with you, haven't I?'

Stipendiary Magistrate D. N. O'Sullivan returned to his court promptly at 2 pm. He smiled wistfully when he saw Barbara standing in the back of the court waiting for her name to be called. A few moments later she was standing in the dock again, telling Mr. O'Sullivan that she had withdrawn the money from her Hull Savings Bank account and would pay it into the court right away. She even expressed an apology for the trouble she had caused. Graas then went quite red when she looked over to him and said, 'I will try to be a good citizen, just like this young bobby said. He's a real sweetie.'

Mr. O'Sullivan glared at her for several seconds, then glanced at Graas, who was standing beside the witness box. He spent several minutes writing in the court register. The court remained silent. There was no one in the public gallery, and still no one in the press seats. Barbara stood motionless in the dock and, fearing the worst, Graas purposely avoided the prosecuting inspector's eye. Eventually Mr. O'Sullivan looked up from his papers and asked Barbara if she was willing to be placed on probation for two years. She readily agreed. Then he looked over at Graas and said, 'There is more than one person taking a chance today with you, Snorthurst. If you fail me I shall keep my promise and send you to Quarter Sessions, and be sure of this, this young officer will also hear the sound of my wrath. Do you understand?'

'I do,' she replied. 'I do.'

Leaving the Guildhall after seeing a probation officer, Barbara asked Graas, 'Why did you put a good word in for me? I would be on my way to Durham prison now if it weren't for you.'

Looking ahead in the hope that one day soon he would be a detective in the CID, Graas replied, 'Maybe one day some serious crime might occur when I need good information. Maybe, just maybe, you will be able to help me; after all, you must know the criminal fraternity in this city better than I do. I don't even know all the streets of this city, let alone the criminals.'

Barbara laughed and said, 'I always thought you coppers were a devious lot, but you are starting early.'

Little did he appreciate it then, but Graas's reasoning behind his good citizen comments was to prove highly beneficial in the years to follow.

Ways and Means

Back in uniform after his highly satisfying and enjoyable spell in plain clothes, Graas was walking his beat about 11 o'clock one night when he watched a ginger-haired youth throw a litterbin full of rubbish on to the pavement beside a bus stop. He caught up with the youth, 'Pick that bin up and all the rubbish and put it back where you took it from!'

'Pick it up yourself!' he replied. 'You can't tell me what to do.' At that moment a more experienced policeman from an adjoining beat joined in. 'Pick it up *now!*,' he ordered loudly.

'You can't make me,' replied Ginger. 'And if you think you can, I can tell you that the last time I was told to something I didn't and the man hit me. He got fined £2 for hitting me. So buzz off!'

The experienced policeman swiftly grabbed Ginger by the collar, held him against the bus stop sign and said, 'Pick it all up. That's a good boy. If you don't do as I say I shall want more than £2 worth. Let's say I'll be happy with, say, at least ten-quids' worth. Do you get the message?'

'All right,' replied Ginger. The policeman let go of his grasp and the youth sheepishly went about picking up the bin and all the rubbish. As he was doing so a man came riding by on a bicycle. 'I don't believe it. What are you doing, son?' he enquired as he pulled up alongside the kerb. 'These two made me pick it all up, dad,' he replied.

'Made you do it? How come? What sort of magic is this? I can't get him to do a damn thing,' said Ginger's dad.

'Oh, you just need to speak to him kind of gently,' explained the experienced policeman.

'Well, I'll be damned,' replied the father. 'I'll wait until you've finished and then we'll go and tell your mother.'

'But he was going to bash me, dad. Honest he was,' Ginger snapped.

'Now then, lad,' said his dad. 'What have I told you about telling lies? Let me hear no more about it! I'm pleased with what I am seeing so we won't spoil it, will we?' Graas and his colleague kept quiet, and Ginger said nothing more but completed his task. He then walked off with his dad, scowling back at the two constables as he made his way home.

'That's policing 1950s style, you see. Something the training school doesn't teach you, young Graas, 'commented the experienced constable. 'If you could stick with me for a week or two you would learn that there are ways and means to apply the law without having to go to court all the time. I didn't spend my time helping to beat the Germans without learning a thing or two about handling things in a commonsense way. The young lads of today won't thank you for taking them to court and getting them a criminal record. A steady hand is all they need. Once we lose command of our authority on the streets we shall lose the general fight against disorder and crime, you know. Mark my words. So long as there are good practical policemen walking the streets, things will be kept in acceptable control.'

'Yes, I understand what you mean,' replied Graas. 'I see that it's easy enough for policemen to walk beats in the more compact areas where houses, shops, schools and streets are close together. I can't see that it will be easy on the large council estates such as Longhill and Greatfield. Can you?'

'No. I hear that we are soon to get Velocette motor bikes and maybe Ford Escort-type vans for covering the beats out there,' he replied. 'They will apparently be equipped with radios similar to those in the Transport Department cars. It's obvious that vehicles of some sort are necessary for the suburban areas, but you know it will signal the end of beat duty, as we know it. Once you put a bobby on a motorbike or into a car you lose practically all contact with the public. Mark my words, lad. As the powers that be take us Bobbies off our feet and give us all transport, the crime and vandalism problems will increase tenfold. I shall not see too much of the change before I retire but you will see crime figures double in the next ten years. They can say what they like about us but the way Hull is policed nowadays at least keeps criminals at bay. Hull City is one of the best police forces in the country. Sidney Lawrence is the one to thank for that. We still have one or two idiots in the job, mind.'

Graas gave much thought to the prophesying, wisdom and experience of his old colleague as they parted company and continued to patrol their adjacent beats that night. The thought of riding about in a car instead of being on foot did sound attractive, however, especially around 2 am that night, when it became cold, damp and dreary as he turned into Cleveland Street. He was often given the Witham, Cleveland Street, or Stoneferry area beats just east of the River Hull for his night duty. They were the least desirable beats in the division, probably because they were drab and slum-like with many of the houses ready for Sam Allon and his demolition men to wipe them off the face of the earth. The people still living there were generally warm-hearted and old-fashioned in their attitude to the bobby on the beat and there were always places where a cup of tea and a chat could be had, even in the early hours of the morning. On a wall at the end of one terrace in St. Mark Street people living in the terrace had painted a huge Union Jack in red, white and blue, with the words, 'Victory. Welcome Home, Lads'. It was now 13 years since the end of World War Two but the painted welcome had stood the test of time and would no doubt remain there until Sam Allon and his men demolished the whole terrace.

It was quiet and still. The late-night merrymakers had made their way home. Hull Corporation late-night buses had long since been garaged up for the night, mostly at the Craven Park bus garage, and the streets seemed fit for nothing but policemen, cats and the odd rat or two. Even the late-night taxis appeared to have ceased their travels. Fog swirled about from the River Hull and across Lime Street but there was a complete silence that made a pleasant change from the general hum of activity that would soon signal the start of another day as cleaners and postmen began their early morning walks to work about half an hour before the first buses took to the road. Cyclists who for a while preferred their bikes to buses would soon join them. Meantime Graas chose to stand in the shadow and shelter of a Cleveland Street doorway.

As he neared the entrance a black cat scurried away from the door where it had been sitting on a well-worn piece of coconut matting. It didn't go far. From across the road another cat appeared. The two of them met almost in the middle of Cleveland Street and then sat within a couple of feet of each other. Graas watched them for a while. The two were joined by a third that came creeping out of Spivey Street. Then two more came from the shadows and joined the group as they gently meowed to each other for a minute or so. They shuffled around until they appeared to be sitting in the shape of a horseshoe. Graas became completely fascinated watching the group as he realised that they were just sitting about 12 feet away, deliberately staring at him in the doorway. With little better to do he shone his torch at them but they simply stared into the torchlight with their eyes seemingly playing out a weird feline ritual. It was rather eerie. He shone his torch to the ground at his feet. There on the coconut matting he could see cat hair galore. That was it, he thought. The matting apparently created a little warmth for the cats at that hour and Graas was standing where the cats wanted to be.

Being an animal lover he decided to move on. He did not want to deprive the cats of their little bit of comfort, especially as it was probably the only time of night when they would not be disturbed in their little friendly get-together. Anyhow, he had to make his way to Chapman Street for his routine call to divisional HQ, so he left the doorway. He walked on for about 30 yards but could not resist a glance back to the cats. As he did so he saw one of the animals make a hurried dash into the doorway, followed by a second and a third. Ah, well, he thought. At least I've made some scraggy cats happy for a while.

When he telephoned Divisional HQ ten minutes later he was instructed to go to a house off Dansom Lane where an elderly woman had apparently been locked out of her home. Odd time of night to be locked out, thought Graas. A watchman at Reckitt's factory in Dansom Lane had telephoned Crowle Street to report the woman's plight so now Graas was striding along Chapman Street and Dansom Lane to see if he could help the lady. As he approached the terrace he saw that several houses were boarded up and empty. Then he saw the woman's house, with its dirty curtains and piece of cardboard covering a broken windowpane. She was huddled down on the doorstep whimpering quietly and shivering uncontrollably, wearing a ragged nightdress, an old woollen cardigan buttoned up to the neck and a pair of dirty, well-worn slippers.

'Hello, Ma,' announced Graas as he approached her. 'Is this your house?'

She looked at him but said nothing as he helped her to her feet. 'You will be catching your death of cold, Ma.' Once more he asked, 'Is this your house?'

She looked up at him and with a scowl said, 'You don't think I'd be sitting here if I didn't live here do you? I just want to get in and then you can clear off.' She continued, 'I don't like coppers so you open my door, that's all. You're not coming in and I don't give coppers cups of tea.'

'Are you sure that the door is locked?' he enquired.

'Of course it's locked. I might be getting on but I know when a door's locked and when it's not. I'm not daft,' she replied.

Graas checked the door. It was locked. 'What about the back door, Ma? Maybe it's unlocked. Shall I try it?' he asked.

'What do you take me for?' she replied angrily. 'I wouldn't be here starving cold if I could get in. Coppers! Good gracious, you young 'uns are hopeless. I knew Detective Superintendent Cocksworth and Detective Inspector Arthur Salvidge in my young days. Now they was good coppers, they was. Real gentlemen if ever there were. Not like you lot today.'

'I've only come to help you, you know. You are shivering with cold and upset; so don't be annoyed with me. Anyway, how have you got yourself locked out? The door is locked and it seems to me that the key is on the inside and locked shut too. How did that happen? Is there someone else in the house?' Graas asked.

'Don't matter who is in the house. It's not your business. I didn't ask for you to come here. The watchman at Reckitt's saw me locked out and said he would get some help. He didn't say anything about getting a copper,' she said.

Ignoring the remark, Graas said, 'I reckon I can force the door open. It doesn't look much of a door. I'll give it a good kick near the lock and it will be open.' With no more thought, he kicked hard at the door with the flat of his foot, and the door swung wide open and jammed against an old piece of scuffed-up rag matting on the floor. The old woman said, 'Now buzz off. I told you, I never asked you here. Go away. We don't like coppers in this terrace.'

At that moment a scruffy middle-aged man appeared in the doorway. He appeared to be under the influence of drink. Graas was only a couple of feet away from him and he could sense the unmistakable smell of whisky. With a fierce look at the old woman the man said, 'What have you done bringing a copper here, mother?'

The old woman appeared unconcerned, shrugged her shoulders, but made no comment.

He turned to the man and said, 'She was locked out and was very upset and shivering with cold. I came to help her.'

'If you've damaged our door you will have to pay for it!' he replied. 'You have no authority to go about kicking people's doors in. I bet you don't have a search warrant.'

'Don't upset him, Albert,' said the woman. 'Look he's a young 'un, can't you see? Just say thank you constable and he'll buzz off. You can't trust young coppers. Haven't I told you that before?'

The smell of whisky coming from Albert's breath and from inside the house roused Graas's curiosity. And why was the old woman so keen to want him to 'buzz off'? The smell of whisky in such a house was unusual, to say the least. It was obvious that the pair did not want Graas around either so he certainly wasn't going to 'buzz off' without knowing more about Albert and his mother.

'Why was your mother locked out, Albert?' asked Graas.

'It's none of your bleeding business. It's my house and she's my mum. What goes on here is private, so clear off!' spluttered Albert as he leaned against the doorframe, half in and half out of the house. Trying to get a good look inside, Graas could see that a candle was burning on an upturned tea chest only a few feet inside the room; but he could see little else.

'Why were you locked out, Ma?' enquired Graas. 'Was Albert's drinking the problem?'

She did not reply.

Directing his question at Albert, Graas said, 'What whisky have you got inside?'

Ignoring the question, Albert spoke to his mother, 'See, I bleeding told you. What were you thinking, bringing a copper to our door?'

'It's your fault, not mine,' she replied. 'If you'd have let me have a drop it would have been alright. But no, you greedy sod. You always think of yourself. Your poor old Mum never gets a look in.' She began to make her way into the house but her son stood solidly in the doorway and, without saying a word, prevented her entry.

'Come on, let her in, you fool. Can't you see she is not dressed to be out in the cold?' Graas said.

'I kicked her out and she's not coming back in. There's nothing you can do about it, so clear off,' he replied. 'You aren't coming in, if that's what you think, not bleeding likely.'

Graas appreciated there was little he could do to make the not-so-bright Albert see sense and let his mother in, but he was not finished. He also realised that Albert was under the influence of drink but he was neither incapable nor disorderly in a public place. He would need to drink more whisky to be incapable and he would need to be out in the street and be disorderly to fulfil the requirements of the drunk and disorderly legislation. And more important still, how much whisky was there in the house – one bottle or ten bottles, and where did it come from?

Graas would be abusing the law if he forced his way into the house: searching without a warrant or without permission could mean trouble for him. He had no chance of getting a search warrant and, if he left the terrace, Albert's suspicions might well have been aroused sufficiently for him to hide whatever whisky there was or get rid of it altogether. Graas had listened intently to other more experienced policemen speak of what they termed the Ways and Means Act, and now felt that he was confronted with a situation that demanded Ways and Means thinking. Yes, he concluded, if Albert were to become disorderly outside his house he could be arrested for being drunk and disorderly in a public place. Then he would have the power to search the house of an arrested person. The power to search was a rather thin balance of power. Disorderliness was not actually a crime to enable a power of search but it was worth a try. Just a bit of shouting from Albert out in the terrace would be enough to arrest him.

How could he get Albert away from the door and, even if he did, how could he get him to start shouting so as to make him disorderly? He could not stand there thinking up a scheme for minutes on end, but he quickly had an idea. It was a pretty rotten idea but he could think of no other. He would walk to the end of the terrace and then shout back to Albert that he would pass word around Hull that would have people thinking that Albert was a police informer. That should get him annoyed and maybe even angry!

As he began to walk towards Dansom Lane, Albert called, 'That's got you, copper. Clear off. You can't tell me what to do. She's staying out and you can't do nowt about it!'

'All right, Albert,' replied Graas. 'Next week, when I am on the afternoon shift I am going to tell one or two of your neighbours that you are a good friend of some of the CID men. In fact, one of your neighbours was arrested for shop breaking a few weeks ago, as no doubt you know. I shall tell his wife that you grassed on him.' With a smile intended to aggravate Albert, he added, 'How about that then?'

Graas hurriedly walked away as he saw Albert grab a milk bottle from the doorstep. Seconds later he heard the sound of footsteps coming up behind and turned to see Albert take a lunge at him with the bottle. Graas instinctively ducked down, the bottle missed him and went crashing on to the pavement. 'You call me a grass and I'll swing for you!' he shouted. He began swearing incoherently. Graas realised that he and he alone had caused the disorderly behaviour and for a split second felt guilty, but was not going to let the feeling of guilt hinder him. This was, after all, the Ways and Means Act at work!

Albert was now disorderly, and there was just enough in his behaviour to say that he was drunk too. With the bottle on the ground in pieces, Graas felt safe to apprehend him and quickly gave him a hammerlock and bar hold on his right arm, forcing the elbow in a slightly unnatural position. 'Mercy, mercy!' shouted Albert. 'If I'd hit you, the bottle would only have got your helmet. It wouldn't bloody kill you.'

'Never mind that, Albert, replied Graas. 'I'm arresting you for being drunk and disorderly but, before we go to telephone for the van to take you to Crowle Street, I am going to find out what whisky you have in that house of yours. Do you understand?'

'You've bloody worked it on me, you have. I was doing no harm 'til you said about grassing. It's diabolical, it is. Never grassed on nobody, me. Never.' moaned Albert.

Graas marched Albert through the open door into his house. By the light of the candle and his torchlight Graas saw that Albert's mother was now sitting just inside the door on an old couch. She was taking a swig from a whisky bottle and appeared content as Graas and Albert entered. 'Can't you put a light on?' asked Graas.

'Lights? We've got no lights. The gas man came and cut us off weeks ago,' Albert's mother grumbled.

'That's right,' added Albert. 'Now you've got in, how about letting go my arm. Can't you see you are bleeding well breaking it?'

'I'm not breaking anything, Albert,' replied Graas as he released his grip. Shining his torch around the small living room he saw a partly opened carton marked 'Bell's Whisky' on a table. A quick glance also revealed that two bottles were missing from the sectioned carton though it contained several more sealed bottles. On the couch beside Albert's mother was a two-lb. large jam jar containing Bank of England £5, £1 and ten-shilling notes. There were also several half crowns, florins, shillings, sixpences, three-penny pieces and other copper coins.

'Well now, Albert. Where is this little lot from?' asked Graas with a self-satisfied smile.

'I'm telling you nowt. You nearly broke my arm, you did,' replied Albert.

'But I didn't break it, Albert. Where did you get this stuff? I shall find out sooner or later,' said Graas earnestly.

'He locked me out, he did,' muttered Albert's mother. 'I only wanted a bottle for myself. Medicine like. He's a good lad but he can be awkward when he's had a bit to drink.'

'How old are you, Albert?' Graas enquired.

Albert did not answer but his mother said. 'He's 48 now, or is it 49. I can't remember. Yes that's about it, he's 49. Never married you know. Lived with me all his life he has. You are 49, aren't you, Albert?'

'If you say so,' he replied.

Albert had quietened down and he looked sad and forlorn in the bleak light of the candle and Graas's torchlight. Graas chose the moment to gently ask again, 'Come on, Albert. Where did you get this stuff?'

Looking dejected, he replied, 'From pub down Waterloo Street. I just hid in toilet when pub closed, then helped myself. You can't do me for breaking in 'cause I was already in when pub was open. I reckoned if I didn't break in you lot couldn't get me for shop breaking and that, so it's not pub breaking. I only broke out and took this stuff with me. Money was in the bar in that jar. Got out through toilet window I did. Last time I was in court they told me if I broke into anywhere again I'd get a long sentence. I didn't break in this time. Make sure you tell the court that 'cause it's true. You will find out when you check pub. Up near Waterloo cinema it is. Sorry about chucking bottle. You shouldn't threaten me saying I'm a grass. It's not fair.'

'All right, Albert,' said Graas. Feeling a little guilty about being the instigator of Albert's disorderly behaviour, he added, 'Now we are getting the whisky and cash sorted out I'm prepared to forget about the bottle throwing and drunk and disorderly bit.' Then he added, 'Remember that you are under arrest. We are now going up to Witham where I shall telephone for transport to take you to Crowle Street police station. I will carry the cash. I want you to carry the carton of whisky.'

Graas allowed Albert's mother to take a swig or two from the bottle she was holding, then took it from her and placed it in the carton. He handed it to Albert saying, 'Take care of it, Albert. You can now carry it to the telephone box in Witham. It's not far. If you drop anything or try any funny business I shall carry out my threat and tell certain people what a good grass you are.'

'You young coppers are hard bastards right enough. I used to be able to cope with getting a thumping like in the old days but I can't cope with this mind-blowing stuff. I would never be a snout, no never. I'd be too scared. Only went to Craven Street school, you know. I was bottom of the class most of the time I was, but all right, I won't mess you about any more,' he replied.

'Now I can get a bit of sleep. He locked me out. Now you are locking him up. Funny old world, ain't it?' his mother announced as she began to settle down on the couch.

A steady walk along Dansom Lane and into Witham took them to the Blenkin Street police telephone pillar just off Witham. With a direct line to Crowle Street, Graas was able to tell the station sergeant about Albert's arrest. Very soon they were on their way to Crowle Street.

The pub licensee was awakened soon after 6 am and, after a check, confirmed the theft of the whisky and £28. 7. 6d from the premises. Albert was committed in custody to Hull Quarter Sessions for trial. He pleaded guilty and was sentenced to 18 months' imprisonment. Nothing ever came to light about the disorderly behaviour and Graas never breathed another word about the threatened grassing.

Walking the same Dansom Lane beat early one evening a few months later, Graas was called to Albert's terrace house by a neighbour who reported that he had not seen Albert's mother for a couple of days. The front door was held shut with a piece of rope that she had apparently fastened to a nail on the inside of the door, with another nail on the door frame allowing the door to open an inch or so only. The bolt had not been repaired from the time Graas had kicked the door open. However, the gap in the doorway was sufficient for Graas to poke his truncheon through to release the rope. Inside he found the room hung with dampness from the smell of the sad and rotting linoleum on the floor. Lying on the couch he found Albert's mother partly covered by an old threadbare, foul smelling ex-army blanket. She had died of natural causes, probably the previous day.

Making his routine telephone call to the station sergeant at Crowle Street shortly afterwards, he reported that the woman was dead. 'You are not qualified to say a person is dead, 129. You can only say a person has stopped breathing and lifeless. Only a qualified person like a vet or a doctor is permitted to say a person is dead,' replied the sergeant.

'This one is stiff and very cold,' replied Graas as he became annoyed and quickly replaced the telephone handset. The phone rang back almost immediately but Graas ignored it, believing that it was only the station sergeant trying to admonish him for his impudence in hanging up on him.

As he walked off into the darkness of the early night and the rising moon he thought long and hard about the poor old woman. No one deserved to die all-alone in that dirty, damp, mean and squalid room. Poor woman. Her, son Albert didn't even say goodbye to her that night when he left the house under arrest. She never saw him again. Now it was too late and he still had several months of his sentence to complete.

Not many years before, she had been a reliable knocker-upper for several Reckitt's workers in the district, a job that had long since receded from modern memory. Now she had gone too.

Revengeful Management

It was four o'clock on a Monday morning. Pc Graas was in the Holderness Road section box writing a crime report about the theft of the prepayment gas and electricity meter cash contents in a house in Craven Street when he received a telephone call from the station sergeant at Crowle Street. 'I have just put you down for duty at two o'clock,' said Sergeant Bagpipes.

'Two o'clock when?' asked Graas.

'Two o'clock this afternoon. It's Monday now. You will be back on duty on your beat at two o'clock. Understand?' said Bagpipes.

'I am presently on duty until six o'clock this morning, sergeant,' replied Graas. 'Are you telling me that I am to be back on duty within eight hours? I must point out that I am due to have a day off after I finish my duty today. It is shown on the monthly duty roster.'

'The day off is cancelled 'cause I have cancelled it,' said Bagpipes. 'Someone has gone sick and we need a replacement. I have decided you will do it. You will now be on duty at two o'clock this afternoon.'

In his normal state of arrogance Bagpipes hung up without waiting to hear anything Graas may have had to say. Feeling tired, and fed up with the lack of decent management, Graas telephoned Bagpipes. A creep of a constable answered the phone call saying that Bagpipes was too busy to speak to him. Graas replied that he would keep telephoning until Bagpipes did have the time to speak and that, if he did not have the decency to answer the calls, Graas would submit a written report to the Superintendent to complain about Bagpipe's lack of management ability. A few moments later Bagpipes telephoned Graas, who was still completing the crime report. 'Report me, would you, 129?' he blasted down the telephone in his broad Scottish accent. 'Do that and you will regret it. I am the station sergeant and you will do what I say. It is an order. You will be back on duty at two o'clock. Do you hear?'

'I get your arrogance, sergeant. I can't fail on that score. However, I simply want to know why you do not have the ability to speak to people reasonably,' replied Graas. Raising his voice and feeling quietly confident, he continued, 'I am due to go off duty at six o'clock, and from what you are telling me – not asking me – I have to be back here at the Holderness Road section box at 1.45 pm ready to be walking the streets again at two o'clock. That is less than eight hours after I have been on night duty. Meantime I am expected to get some sleep and be fit for whatever happens this afternoon and evening. I shall do it, but under protest. I think your management style stinks. No wonder the police has a problem in recruitment. People like you do nothing at all to encourage good policing, let alone recruitment.'

Graas then took considerable delight in reciprocating Bagpipes behaviour by hanging up on him abruptly before he had a chance to reply. With a feeling of satisfaction he also left the section box in order to avoid any further telephone calls and Bagpipe's sharp tongue.

Graas returned for duty at 1.45 pm after a period of spasmodic sleep. His usual enthusiasm for the job was becoming blunted, though, and he felt that he had perhaps overdone his comments. He decided that he had spoken the truth, however, and, as always, he leaned on the truth to help him keep abreast of any retaliation that might come from Bagpipes.

On his first routine call to Crowle Street that afternoon he received word that he had been allocated to be working the 6 am to 2 pm shift the following day. That meant another quick change of duty, leaving him a mere eight hours between shifts again. He couldn't believe it. There was hardly any time for sleep and rest again. 'When was this change of duty arranged?' Graas enquired.

'Oh, Bagpipes finalised the week's duties before he went off duty this morning,' replied a constable, who sometimes worked in the office with Bagpipes.

'When is Bagpipes on duty again?' asked Graas.

'He's off for a couple of days now,' replied the constable.

A short while afterwards Graas spoke to a constable who lived near Bagpipes. 'You don't seem your usual self this afternoon,' said the constable.

'No, I am not,' replied Graas. 'I didn't finish duty until six this morning. Now I am on duty two to ten. Believe it or not, I have just been told that I have to be back again at six in the morning, leaving me with less than eight hours between going off duty at ten tonight and coming back on duty again at 5.45 in the morning. It's not good enough and I intend to do something about it.'

'Be careful,' replied the constable. 'I happen to know that you annoyed old Bagpipes last week when you submitted about a dozen summonses. You see, you gave him a lot of work to do getting them all typed up and submitting them for process. He was heard to grumble about having to process them and he was heard to say that he would sort you out!'

'Good grief,' replied Graas. 'So that's what it's all about. I shall give him as well as I get from him. I shall go and demand to see the Chief Constable, that's what I'll do.'

'Oh, no. Don't do that. The Chief will not see you,' replied the constable. 'There are other ways to aggravate Bagpipes. He's got a telephone in his house now, you know. And I know, living near him, that after night duty he sleeps well into the afternoon. Give him a ring and, when he answers, hang up. It will disturb his sleep and make him real grumpy for the rest of the day.'

'He hasn't mentioned the summonses to me. Are you sure he was annoyed about them?' enquired Graas. 'After all, I had no choice but issue those summonses. Two involved driving without due care and attention and failing to give way at a pedestrian crossing where a woman was badly injured by a car not stopping. The others were quite serious matters too.'

Still feeling sore about Bagpipes' attitude and thinking about the anonymous telephone call suggestion, Graas began to experience a sense of mischief in his mind and did something he had never done before. In the presence of his constable colleague, he made an anonymous telephone call to Bagpipes' home from a telephone box at the corner of Southcoates Lane and Holderness Road. Bagpipes' wife answered the call saying that her husband was asleep and that he never liked being disturbed from his slumbers after night duty. Putting on an accent he thought similar to that of the Crowle Street Chief Inspector and identifying himself as that Chief Inspector, he demanded that Bagpipes come to the telephone immediately. Controlling his mirth as much as possible, Graas waited a minute or so before Bagpipes came to the phone. 'Yes, sir. I am sorry to keep you waiting, sir,' he said. With that the two constables could contain themselves no longer and simply burst out laughing before replacing the telephone handset. So a brief moment of childish self-satisfaction was achieved.

Graas felt quite guilty afterwards and realised that he was stooping as low with his telephone call as was Bagpipes with his management. He decided he would not make any more anonymous calls.

Unable to do anything about the awful changes of duty, Graas worked the two shift changes as ordered but he was so incensed with Bagpipes' that he began to believe that the sergeant's incredibly poor management was something he was not going to suffer much more. It was a few days later when he met up with Pc Roy Lindop, one of the most sensible policemen he was ever to meet. Pc Lindop had joined the force in 1953, roughly four years before Graas arrived in Hull. Graas told Roy Lindop that he was seriously thinking about leaving the force, but the wise Pc Lindop said that he should delay doing such a thing as the general view many constables had was that Graas would be going into the CID once his probationary two years was complete. Graas hoped that that would be so, but he did not know if he could wait long enough. He also considered writing to the Police Federation representative about Bagpipes but was advised that the Federation at that time was very weak due mainly to the ever-threatening hold the Chief Constable had over everyone in the force.

However, despite feeling life under Bagpipes was far from pleasant and that the discipline of life in uniform was irksome, he delayed doing anything rash. He took Roy Lindop's advice, advice which was to prove of great benefit in the years to follow.

About a week later, Graas saw the friendly Inspector McWhoo again. He had returned from a week's annual leave in Scotland. 'How are you, 129?' he said as he came riding along Williamson Street on his bicycle.

'I have had a glorious time up in Edinburgh. You should go up there some time.'

'I shall one day, if ever I get sufficient time off, sir,' replied Graas. 'I am far from happy with my lot at the moment. I have been messed about by having my shift duties changed with little or no warning recently. I have been considering leaving the force but a constable who has a damn sight more common sense than the majority of sergeants here has suggested that I should hold on and not do anything in haste.'

'I know of the problem, 129,' replied McWhoo. 'One of the sergeants has a thing about you. You see, unknown to you, you summonsed one of his friends recently and it has annoyed him. He was thinking of asking you to drop the summons but he felt that you would think it unfair and would probably complain to higher authority. So he has been taking it out of you by changing your shifts. I only got to know about it on my return from leave. Don't worry, 129. The less said the better, but it won't happen again. I can assure you. Anyhow, the sergeant is retiring soon.'

A Hopeless Case

It was raining heavily and Pc Graas was standing in the darkness of a closed shop doorway doing his best to keep dry. It was about 11.30 pm and several people hurried past without noticing him there. Looking at his watch, he saw it would be another six and a half hours before he could cycle home and get some sleep. It was well known in the force that good heavy rain mixed with the smoke and grime of the night air was probably the best crime prevention there was. Thieves, like everyone else, did not like getting wet and, with everyone hurrying home, little was likely to happen so the night was going to be long, dreary and boring. Graas began thinking about his future. He was nearing the end of his two years' probationary period and he dreamed about the chance of being posted to the CID. But how could he achieve his aim? He had never had a look-in when there was the occasional serious crime, as the CID always took over. He had once mentioned his ambition to one old constable who told him that being in the CID meant spending long hours of work with no recompense and that, unless one was willing to spend much time in public houses mixing with undesirables, there was little chance of success as a detective.

As he was about to leave the shelter of the shop entrance he saw his sergeant pop out of a dark alley some 50 yards away, take a quick look up and down the road and then disappear into the alley again. Graas could not believe it. He had never seen a policeman with an umbrella before and, if his eyes were serving him correctly, the sergeant was there in full uniform holding an umbrella up to keep dry. Maybe his helmet was leaking, who knows? He had obviously not seen Graas in the darkened shop entrance. Graas stood still and quiet. Whatever was Sergeant Norman Case up to? Several minutes had passed when an elderly man shuffled into the doorway beside Graas. 'Hello, Mr. Policeman,' he said, 'I have just seen that Sergeant Case peeping out of that passage down the road. I reckon he's keeping an eye out for you. He's a bit of a nut case you know. He tried to get me done some years ago. Don't like him, me. He tried to make out I had nicked some stuff from Reckitt's. Stuff I had bought from Reckitt's it was, just shoe polish. Nowt to do with him. I reckon he was trying to get into the CID he was, but he's no chance. He hasn't got what it takes for that sort of work. I told one of your old bosses – a chap called Kilvington – about him. He agreed with me that he would never make a CID man in a million years. Too damn regimental and daft he is. Was in the army in the war, but never front line. Reckon he was a pen pusher or an admin wallah. Anyway, I know enough about him to know he's always trying to catch young bobbies out smoking or having a sly cup of tea on duty. I'd just stand here real quiet like. You are in the dry, he's standing in that alley in the rain, but you know what? He's got a bloody umbrella up. Never seen a bobby with an umbrella up before. He's a right wet. Wet on wet, see,' he said with a chuckle. 'Well I'll be off then. The missus will be wondering where I've got to.' Then he shuffled off into the darkness without another word.

Graas stood where he was for several minutes before he decided to continue his beat and walk in the direction of the sergeant's apparent hiding place. As he neared the alley Sergeant Case stepped out of the shadows. 'Ah, 129. You didn't expect to see me out here in the rain, did you? he said. 'Like the umbrella. Pity they don't give us umbrellas as an official issue and part of our uniform.'

'It's enough carrying a whistle, handcuffs, a truncheon and this heavy uniform without a sissy-looking brolly, sergeant. Anyhow, I did expect to see you sometime tonight, sergeant. I haven't seen any supervisory officer so far tonight,' Graas replied.

'You have almost completed your probation, 129, so we feel that we can let you get on with your job these days. It has been noted that you lost your arrest for crime virginity some time ago. And you have been to court with numerous summonses. You have also been involved in at least one sudden death case and several scuffles with drunks and shown that you can handle yourself. Yes. I believe you are on your way to being as good a policeman as I am. Well done.'

Graas chose to ignore the pretentiousness of the sergeant's last remark but said, 'Just a minute, sergeant. Why do you find it necessary to say that I have "lost my arrest for crime virginity"? It seems a rather strange way of saying simply that I have made arrests for crime and have done with it,' asked Graas inquisitively.

'It is appreciated in the force that I have a good command of the English language, 129. I consider it necessary to be as graphic as the human mind will allow when I am speaking,' he replied. 'I should have been in the Education Corps in the war, but they only gave me an admin job. Nowadays I use my knowledge of our language to the betterment of everyone I come into contact with. I was in court not so long ago and when I explained a particular incident to the magistrate he told me that I would do well to explain things in simple English. You see I used the word lugubriously. He asked me to explain what I meant and I told him it meant slyly. He laughed, and from then on did not seem to agree with anything I said. I used good sound educated words too. Anyway, he found the accused not guilty and appeared annoyed with me. Goodness knows why.'

'I don't accept that lugubrious means sly, sergeant,' replied Graas.

'Of course it does,' said the tall, stupid but remarkably refined-looking sergeant.

'Look it up, sergeant. I am sure that you will find it means doleful, you know, being dreary or dismal. How did lugubriously come into your evidence? asked Graas with a certain amount of amusement.

'Oh, I don't remember now. It was some time ago. Anyway, I am not talking about it any more. I have work to do. Let me examine your notebook for a start.'

Graas handed his notebook over to the sergeant grudgingly. He looked at it and signed it before handing it back. Graas had seen that the sergeant was not on his bicycle as usual so he asked why. 'The inspector is busy at Crowle Street with a drunk in charge of a car and with other reports so he has allowed me to use the divisional car for a while tonight. I have left it down a side street so that I can walk about this area checking you beat men for half an hour. Then I shall be driving it over to Marfleet,' he answered.

Shortly afterwards he left Graas and walked off into the rain along Holderness Road, umbrella waving about just above the top of his helmet.

Ten minutes later Graas was writing the details of a missing person into his notebook at the Holderness section box when Sergeant Case came hurrying in. 'Come on, 129,' he shouted. 'I need your help. Some swine has stolen the car. I left it down Balfour Street and now it has gone. Get on your bike and get looking for it. It can't be far away.'

'Did you leave it locked up?' Graas enquired.

'Of course I did. I've got the keys here in my pocket,' Case replied.

'Well, don't you think that you had better telephone Crowle Street and the operations room at Queens Gardens and report it stolen, sergeant, 'Graas asked.

'Do you think I am mad, 129? exclaimed Case. 'I have been entrusted with the vehicle by the inspector. Now it has been stolen. If I circulate it as stolen I will look like an idiot. I shall end up working on a bike forever more or even worse. I shall borrow one of the bikes here. You get off on yours. I shall search the streets on the north side of Holderness Road and you search those on the south side. Be off with you. We shall meet here again in 20 minutes and then decide what to do next.'

'But it could be well away from here now, sergeant. In fact, it could be across the other side of the City by now,' commented Graas.

'It will be if you don't get out there and look for it,' replied the increasingly annoyed sergeant.

Graas got his bicycle from the yard at the back of the section box and rode off as far as Southcoates railway crossing near Waller Street, He decided to check all the streets east of Waller Street, Craven Street, Arundell Street, Balfour Street, Victor Street, Holland Street and so on as far as he could in the 20 minutes Sergeant Case had given him. There was no sign of the black Ford Anglia in Waller Street or Craven Street. In fact, Graas felt that the search was rather pointless because he believed that if anyone had taken the vehicle it would have been driven well away by then. However, the sergeant had detailed him to search those streets and that is what he had to do. In and out of Arundell Street, Balfour Street and Victor Street he pedalled. There was no sign of the car.

Realising that he only had a few minutes of the allotted time before reporting back to the sergeant, Graas cycled into Holland Street with the intention of going back to the section box to insist that Sergeant Case report the missing vehicle for circulation throughout the City and beyond. There in Holland Street, much to his surprise, was the black Ford police car. It was parked bout 50 yards down the street near to a street lamp, facing Holderness Road. The doors were locked and the engine was cold. There was no sign of damage.

Graas was delighted with his find but he was also disturbed. Had the vehicle been stolen at all, he wondered. He cycled back to the section box where he found Case pacing up and down in the backyard under his umbrella. 'We have a right problem on our hands, 129,' he announced as Graas dismounted his bicycle. 'Hey, steady on, sergeant. It is you who has the problem, not me. Don't count me in it. Leaving the vehicle where you did is nothing to do with me,' said Graas, who then asked, 'Where did you leave the vehicle exactly?'

'If you must know I parked it in Balfour Street facing Holderness Road. I parked it near a street lamp where it could be seen and about fifty yards down the street,' he replied.

With a broad smile on his face, and not wanting to prolong Case's agony any more, Graas announced, 'I have found your car, sergeant. It is parked in Holland Street and it seems to me that that is where you left it. It is not damaged at all and the engine is cold, so in my opinion it is not stolen at all.'

'Goodness me, 129. But have you entered the details in your notebook?' asked Case.

'Yes, well, I entered the vehicle registration number. You are always on about keeping notebooks up to date,' replied Graas.

'Entered it in pencil, I hope?' enquired Case. 'Yes, of course I have,' answered Graas.

'Good man. Now come inside and let me have a look at your notebook. We don't want any official record of this incident, do we? I have a rubber. I shall rub your entry out and then all will be well,' said Case patronisingly.

As they entered the section box Sergeant Case folded his umbrella, took his helmet off and sat down. Graas saw that Case's brow was sweating profusely. His grey thinning hair was also soaked in perspiration. Balls of sweat were flooding down to his eyebrows and remained there like droplets of snot about to drop from the neglected nose of an old tramp. For the first time in his life Graas realised that that was exactly what eyebrows were for, they were there as a kind of stop-gap to prevent over-anxious policemen's eyes being flooded with sweat when they took their helmets off.

Sergeant Case reached out to take Graas's notebook from him, 'Just what are you playing at, sergeant? No one rubs anything out of my notebook,' said Graas. 'The official notebook instructions – printed inside the front cover – make it perfectly clear, among other things, that under no circumstances must a page be taken out of a notebook or any erasure made. Any erasure, no matter how good, will show up under inspection and I am the one would have to answer for it in my book. I think, quite frankly, that if any erasure was found you would never back me up by saying that you did it. So, no, you are not rubbing anything out.'

'Be careful, 129. Be careful,' said Case. Then he asked pathetically, 'What have you entered in that book anyway?'

'As a matter of fact, all I have entered at the moment, and all that I have had time for is to enter the registration number of the vehicle, that's all,' replied Graas.

'Well,' said the sergeant, 'it's alright then. You have written the number down as a matter of interest because you know I am using the car, so you have no need to worry.'

'I am not worried, sergeant,' replied Graas. 'I do think you had better be more careful in future, you know. It is clear to me that you forgot where you left the car, and, thinking that you left it in Balfour Street, but not finding it there, you panicked. If you applied yourself in the same way as most other supervisory officers, instead of sneaking around like a weasel trying to catch constables gossiping and so on, you would be much better off.'

'All right, 129,' replied Case as he began to raise his voice. 'Enough is enough. You have had your say. Just you remember how wise I was in not reporting it as stolen until it was absolutely necessary. Think of the fuss it would have caused.'

'That's absolute rubbish, sergeant, and you know it,' said Graas. 'You did not want to circulate it because you were scared of the repercussions if it had been stolen. I reckon you also realised that maybe your memory might be failing you as well. And that's another reason why you didn't want to circulate it straight away. Another point, please don't insult me by trying to cover up your tatty action by telling me that you were wise in not circulating it until absolutely necessary. Being wise is being sensible, prudent, sagacious and so on. Forgetfulness does not mean wisdom. Also if I were you I would ask your wife to buy you a dictionary for your birthday or something and get her to buy you a thesaurus as well.'

'We've got a dictionary in the loft somewhere, but what did you say – a thes . . . something. Oh, it doesn't matter, I'll look it up in the dictionary,' Case replied thoughtfully.

About an hour later Graas saw Sergeant Case park the police car on Holderness Road under Craven Street bridge. He got out of the vehicle and hurriedly walked up to Graas who was standing a few yards away. 'You know about cars, 129. I know because your record shows that you were driving Landrovers in Belfast in the RAF. You see, I have a problem.

A red light keeps coming on on the dashboard of this damned car. What do you think?'

Graas replied, 'It sounds like the ignition light. I would take it to the transport garage at Queens Gardens and have it seen to. I can only guess it will get you there without any trouble.'

'Have a look at it, 129. Come on, have a look,' pleaded Case.

Graas went over to the car with Case, who switched the engine on. The ignition light remained on after the engine started. 'Yes. I would get it to the garage. Have them check the electrics. It's probably only a faulty switch,' advised Graas.

Sergeant Case replied, 'Yes, thank you, that is what I was thinking.' He then did a U-turn and drove off towards the City centre.

Less than 10 minutes later, Case pulled up alongside Graas again. 'If I report this ignition light problem the inspector will think it is my fault, so I am not reporting it,' he said as he sat in the driving seat looking as pompous as ever. 'No, I have a better idea. You can't see the red light now. You see I have put a piece of sticky black tape on the dashboard where the light was showing. Now I can't see it so it's no problem. I'll take the tape off when I've finished with the car.'

'You know, sergeant,' said Graas. 'I can't help but feel exasperated both by your incompetence as a policeman and your pretentiousness as a person. How do you get away with it?'

Sergeant Case shook his head violently as if a wasp had stuck in his ear, then he said, 'I am a sergeant, 129. Don't speak to me like that. In fact, don't ever speak to me like that again.' Then he drove off, obviously ignorant of the ignition light problem.

Graas continued his beat, wondering whoever saw fit to promote such a man some years before. He had heard that Case had once been knocked dateless in a pub brawl outside the Earl De Grey public house. Perhaps that had affected him, or was the knockout blow given by someone who could not stand his pretentious nature?

A few days later, shortly after Graas had left a spell of point duty at North Bridge, Inspector McWhoo came riding up to him on his bicycle. Following the customary salutes McWhoo was so fond of, he said, 'I have been checking your probation records, 129. It's looking very good for you. Your two years' probation is practically at an end. I hope that you have enjoyed it all.'

'Yes, it has been quite an education, sir,' replied Graas. 'I have come across some really fine policemen and no doubt it is thanks to such men that crime and general policing in this city is held in such high regard.'

'Well most of us try our best, 129. I have told you before I am proud to be associated with the way the Chief has changed things since he came here. You may not know it, 129, but, we had a chief constable called Tosh Wells before Mr. Lawrence came here. Wells was hopeless, 'he said. 'He spent most of his time with the boxing crowd in the City and he had many sleazy friends. He came here early in the war and stayed until about 1948 when the police committee got rid of him. There are loads of stories about him. On one occasion he went into the East Riding and pinched a Christmas tree. Just lopped it off the top of a bigger tree, he did. Often under the influence of drink he was too, to say nothing of his misuse of police cars and petrol. Thanks to the Home Office and some members of the police authority, Sidney Lawrence took Wells' place and things began to change for the good in no time. We still have a few nincompoop sergeants left from former days, but even the Stipendiary Magistrate has described the force as splendid. Makes you feel proud to be a policeman here nowadays.'

'I agree, sir,' replied Graas. 'I have met my fair share of what you describe as nincompoops, you know.'

'I would accept that we have one or two sergeants of that kind in the division even today,' replied McWhoo. 'I told one who you know to stop being so priggish the other day. He complained, thought I was calling him a pig. Never mind he will be retiring soon.'

The Inspector rode off on his bicycle but returned shortly afterwards saying, 'I trust you don't include me in that nincompoop description, 129. I would hope that you have forgotten that thing about the VD.'

'I have, sir,' replied Graas.

Graas completed his two years on probation on the first day of 1959. It was the year the London to Birmingham M1 motorway was opened, and the Austin and Morris mini motorcar was introduced. It was also the year the Litter Act made it an offence to drop litter and the year the Humber Bridge Bill received the Royal Assent. 1959 also introduced 48 new recruits to the force. They included five much-needed policewomen. Pc Graas also achieved his ambition to become a detective. He was transferred to the CID in Queens Gardens.